Adapting Transport to Climate Change and Extreme Weather

Implications for Infrastructure Owners and Network Managers

Research Report

This work is published under the responsibility of the Secretary-General of the OECD. The opinions expressed and arguments employed herein do not necessarily reflect the official views of OECD member countries.

This document and any map included herein are without prejudice to the status of or sovereignty over any territory, to the delimitation of international frontiers and boundaries and to the name of any territory, city or area.

Please cite this publication as:
ITF (2016), *Adapting Transport to Climate Change and Extreme Weather: Implications for Infrastructure Owners and Network Managers*, ITF Research Reports, OECD Publishing, Paris.
http://dx.doi.org/10.1787/9789282108079-en

ISBN 978-92-82-10806-2 (print)
ISBN 978-92-82-10807-9 (PDF)

Series: ITF Research Reports
ISSN 2518-6744 (print)
ISSN 2518-6752 (online)

The statistical data for Israel are supplied by and under the responsibility of the relevant Israeli authorities. The use of such data by the OECD is without prejudice to the status of the Golan Heights, East Jerusalem and Israeli settlements in the West Bank under the terms of international law.

Photo credits: Cover © Oliver Clarke.

Corrigenda to OECD publications may be found on line at: *www.oecd.org/about/publishing/corrigenda.htm*.

The International Transport Forum

The International Transport Forum is an intergovernmental organisation with 57 member countries. It acts as a think tank for transport policy and organises the Annual Summit of transport ministers. ITF is the only global body that covers all transport modes. The ITF is politically autonomous and administratively integrated with the OECD.

The ITF works for transport policies that improve peoples' lives. Our mission is to foster a deeper understanding of the role of transport in economic growth, environmental sustainability and social inclusion and to raise the public profile of transport policy.

The ITF organises global dialogue for better transport. We act as a platform for discussion and pre-negotiation of policy issues across all transport modes. We analyse trends, share knowledge and promote exchange among transport decision-makers and civil society. The ITF's Annual Summit is the world's largest gathering of transport ministers and the leading global platform for dialogue on transport policy.

The Members of the ITF are: Albania, Armenia, Argentina, Australia, Austria, Azerbaijan, Belarus, Belgium, Bosnia and Herzegovina, Bulgaria, Canada, Chile, China (People's Republic of), Croatia, Czech Republic, Denmark, Estonia, Finland, France, Former Yugoslav Republic of Macedonia, Georgia, Germany, Greece, Hungary, Iceland, India, Ireland, Israel, Italy, Japan, Korea, Latvia, Liechtenstein, Lithuania, Luxembourg, Malta, Mexico, Republic of Moldova, Montenegro, Morocco, the Netherlands, New Zealand, Norway, Poland, Portugal, Romania, Russian Federation, Serbia, Slovak Republic, Slovenia, Spain, Sweden, Switzerland, Turkey, Ukraine, the United Kingdom and the United States.

International Transport Forum
2, rue André Pascal
F-75775 Paris Cedex 16
contact@itf-oecd.org
www.itf-oecd.org

ITF Research Reports

Foreword

Transport infrastructure represents a significant sunken public and private investment that is fundamental to the functioning of society. These assets are often long-lived and, if regularly maintained, are designed to deliver specified and predictable services over their entire lifetime. Hazards that may degrade asset performance or interrupt network services are generally well-known and are accounted for in transport infrastructure, network planning and design. Thus, even though the natural variability of extreme weather events have sometimes caused significant disruption, these risks were knowable and their impacts have historically been mitigated. With climate change, this is no longer true. This report reviews the range of threats to transport system performance that are posed by climate change and provides guidance to transportation asset owners and network managers to help ensure asset integrity and contribute to continued network performance.

This report benefitted from the contributions of many individuals. Substantial inputs to the work were provided by Butch Wlaschin, Chair of the Working Group, Bill Dwyer, Arianne Dupont-Keiffer, Matthew Karlaftis, Gabrielle Grimm and Denis François. The report's principal authors were Pekka Leviäkangas (Chapters 2 and 3), Michael Taylor (Chapter 3) and Philippe Crist (Chapters 1, 2, 3, 4 and 5). Shinri Sone and the Institute for National Institute for Land and Infrastructure Management (Japan) hosted an invaluable Working Group seminar and a series of technical visits. Dominique Bouquet provided essential support throughout the course of the project and Liv Gudmundson capably edited the report.

Table of contents

Figures

Tables

Abbreviations

AASHTO	American Association of State Highway and Transportation Officials
AOGCM	Atmosphere-ocean general circulation models
CBA	Cost-benefit analysis
CIRIA	Construction, Industry, Research and Information Association
CO_2	Carbon Dioxide
DfT	UK Department for Transport
ENSO	El Niño-Southern Oscillation
ESM	Earth system models
FHWA	US Federal Highways Administration
GHG	Greenhouse gases
IPCC	Intergovernmental Panel on Climate Change
NHS	Australian National Highway System
RCP	Representative concentration pathway
ROA	Real option analysis
RDM	Robust decision making
SRES	Special Report on Emission Scenarios
TRB	Transportation Research Board

Units of measure

°C	Celsius
Ppm	Parts per million
mm yr	Millimetres per year

Executive summary

Findings

Broad evidence indicates that man-made emissions of greenhouse gases are changing the climate, and many of the potential impacts of climate change on meteorological conditions can affect the performance of transport systems and the viability of transport infrastructure. Summer temperatures will increase and heat extremes will become more frequent and last longer. Winter temperatures will become milder but temperature amplitudes may increase and swings between sub-zero and above freezing point temperatures will occur more often. Warming of the Arctic regions will lead to deeper permafrost melting (and soil heaving) with loss of summer sea and land ice. Winters will see more precipitation in the Northern Hemisphere, and more of it will be rain.

Large parts of the Southern lower Northern Hemispheres may become dryer on average. Extreme precipitation events will become stronger and more frequent, even in regions with lower average levels of rainfall. The strength of extreme storms may increase, especially for extra-tropical cyclones and Arctic cyclones. Sea levels will rise, with more frequent wave overtopping and thus contributing to more damaging storm surges. In some instances, sea level rise may permanently flood low-lying areas. Finally, more CO_2 in the atmosphere will accelerate the deterioration of concrete whereas more elevated levels of carbon dioxide in seawater will increase damage to submerged and exposed infrastructure elements.

Adapting transport infrastructure to these expected changes is complicated by the fact that model-based projections of future climate are ill-adapted for use by transport asset owners and network managers. First, scientific models of climate change rarely provide specific insight regarding specific impacts at discrete locations. Second, model projections are not as reliable as historic meteorological data and cannot be used as equivalent in planning for infrastructure, as they do not address some key uncertainties.

Meteorological and climate factors fall into the range of manageable risks that asset managers must contend with thus these historic variables are embedded in both the siting of transport networks and the design specifications of specific assets. This ensures that infrastructure continues to operate under a range of expected meteorological conditions and weather phenomena. Even though the natural variability of extreme weather events may cause significant disruption, if asset owners have undertaken due diligence in both the planning and design phases of infrastructure deployment, these risks are generally well known and are more-or-less contained.

Under a changing climate, however, meteorological and climate parameters can evolve in uncertain ways and thus make the consequences for transport networks more difficult to predict. This uncertainty entails the risk of either over-specification of infrastructure design standards (leading to unproductive investments) or under-specification (leading to asset failure or service degradation). For public authorities tasked with delivering quality transport services or private operators who must realise expected returns for their investors, these are considerable risks, and new models for decision making under uncertainty are required to ensure continued and reliable transport network performance in the face of climate change.

Policy insights

Act now to preserve the value of transport infrastructure and maintain network performance

For assets whose design life or effective period of use extends to 50-plus years, the potential exposure to climate hazards is significant. Here planners today will already have to seek ways to assess more comprehensively whether their plans for transport infrastructure, including siting decisions, are robust to a wide range of potential impacts from climate change. For less long-lived assets, network managers must anticipate climate impacts when renewing infrastructure.

Protect transport infrastructure against climate impacts through good maintenance

Maintenance reduces vulnerability to climate impacts and is a powerful hedging strategy in the face of climate change. Postponing maintenance on the expectation that it will not necessarily lead to immediate infrastructure failure is no longer acceptable, as the cumulative impact of deferred maintenance increases the likelihood of disruptions. Sensors and communication technology can help target maintenance on when and where it is needed.

Prepare for more frequent and unexpected failure of transport infrastructure

Under climate change, asset managers should plan for scenarios in which multiple hazards lead to unexpected or cascading failures. With connected networks and systems, disruptions can propagate beyond the initially affected infrastructure to other vital transport and non-transport systems. Co-located infrastructure poses special risks that must be anticipated and mitigated, for instance a bridge that carries road and rail traffic as well as hosting water, fiber optic and electric conduits. Preparing for these hazard scenarios requires improved co-operation and communication among stakeholders.

Account for temporary unavailability of transport assets in in service continuity plans

Extreme weather events may make transport infrastructure temporarily unavailable without significantly damaging it - for instance short-lived flooding of rail lines or gantry cranes forced to cease operation due to high winds. Robust service continuity plans for such scenarios should be in place and include re-routing, use of other modes and plans to rapidly bring the asset back online.

Assess vulnerability of transport assets and networks from climate change and extreme weather

Vulnerability assessments allow prioritisation adaptation efforts based on potential consequences. They must address vulnerabilities at both asset and network level. Risk analysis is a core component of this exercise. Asset managers must ask themselves "What can happen?", "How likely is that?" and "What are the consequences?".

Focus on transport system resilience, not just on designing robust infrastructure.

Resilience-based approaches accept asset failure as an unwanted but occasionally unavoidable consequence of climate change. Rather than avoiding failure completely, resilience-based approaches focus on minimising the consequences of an asset becoming unavailable. This means moving away from the passive defence of infrastructure to establishing proactive processes that minimise system down-time, for instance by include contingency planning that allows for safe failure of assets.

Re-evaluate thinking on redundant transport infrastructure

Network redundancy has value where more asset failures may occur as the result of climate change. This may go counter to reducing "wasteful" redundancy and will require new methodologies for assessing the value of redundancy. Any assessment of network robustness should include operation during a crisis as well as recovery from failure of critical links. It should also account for lack of alternative routes and demand-weighted importance of each link. Robustness assessments incorporating alternative transport modes can help to better preserve transport service levels during disruptions.

Do not rely solely on cost-benefit analysis for appraising the value of transport infrastructure

Cost-benefit analysis (CBA) is useful where the probability of future climate impacts can be robustly assessed and impacts quantified. Risk-adjusted discount rates and providing decision makers with explicit assessments of climate-related uncertainties can help improve CBA. Yet many climate change impacts are subject to deep uncertainty and cannot be assigned objective or subjective probabilities. Likewise, agreement on other inputs to CBA may be difficult to obtain in light of a changing climate. These shortcomings limit the usefulness of cost-benefit appraisal as a stand-alone approach to guide transport investments for long-lived infrastructure.

Develop new decision-support tools that incorporate deep uncertainty into asset appraisal

Appraisal techniques such as Real Option Analysis (ROA) which is particularly suited for large, up-front and irreversible investments, or Robust Decision Making (RDM), which is specifically adapted to situations where no probabilistic information on impacts or outcomes exists, offer complementary approaches to CBA. ROA captures the value of flexibility in both to the timing of an investment decision ("build now" vs "build later") as well as to the ability for the infrastructure to adjust to changing conditions over time (e.g. "build for, but not with"). RDM favours outcomes that are optimal in no single situation but that are good enough in most circumstances and thus seeks to minimise regrets rather than optimise specific but potentially vulnerable outcomes. Yet neither ROA nor RDM are currently being used for project appraisal for transport infrastructure, and work remains to be done to understand how they can best be integrated into transport investment appraisal.

Chapter 1. The potential effects of climate change on transport infrastructure

Much of the understanding of the linkages between human-caused emissions of greenhouse gases and other anthropogenic climate changes is based on complex climate models that have generally performed well in tracking current global temperatures. Nonetheless, these models are approximations (albeit very sophisticated ones) that cumulate several possible sources of errors. This chapter will discuss in general terms the current scientific state of understanding of the direction and scope of climate change and how these changes may give rise to transport infrastructure or network service-damaging hazards. It also addresses the extent with which confidence can or should be ascribed to projections of future hazards such as temperature change, sea level rise, changes in precipitation, etc.

The United Nations Intergovernmental Panel on Climate Change (IPCC) has identified anthropogenic emissions of greenhouse gases (GHG) as the primary driver behind significant and potentially critical changes in global climate on the basis of wide-ranging empirical evidence, observations and model-based analysis (IPCC, 2013).

Though climate models are imperfect predictors of complex climate system dynamics, there is little systemic evidence or analysis that points to future climatic patterns that are substantially different or counter to the trends depicted by the bulk of models used to underpin the IPCC analysis. Nonetheless, the scientific understanding of climate change continues to evolve. The current state of knowledge is characterised by areas where the science is well understood and accepted, areas where there is a general consensus but continued debate and areas characterised by substantial uncertainty.

In addition, while broad evidence seems to support the view that man-made emissions of greenhouse gases may be responsible for climate change, there remains considerable uncertainty over the exact scale, scope and regional impacts of climate change which complicates policy making. Both levels of uncertainty – on the science and on the impacts – are relevant for transport since addressing climate change should aim for synergy between transport and climate policy goals and ensure that trade-offs between these objectives are undertaken knowingly and transparently.

Box 1.1. **IPCC Working Group I input to the Fifth Assessment Report - Climate change: The physical science basis**

Released in September 2013, the input of the United Nations Intergovernmental Panel on Climate Change (IPCC) Working Group I to the IPCC's Fifth Assessment Report assesses the current state of scientific understanding regarding climate change. It reviews the physical science basis, discusses climate change processes and seeks to clarify knowledge on the imputation and potential scale and scope of climate change. It captures the most current state of scientific knowledge relevant to climate change at the time of its release. According to this report: "Warming of the climate system is unequivocal, and since the 1950s, many of the observed changes are unprecedented over decades to millennia. The atmosphere and ocean have warmed, the amounts of snow and ice have diminished, sea level has risen and the concentrations of greenhouse gases have increased" (IPCC, 2013).

The climate change transport infrastructure impact pathway

Of the six so-called greenhouse gases,[1] three play a predominant role given their volume of emissions (carbon dioxide) and/or elevated warming potential (methane and nitrous oxide). The emission of these gases leads to an observed or modelled series of interactions that have an impact on global average temperatures, weather patterns and, ultimately, human societies (see Figure 1.1). Figure 1.1 illustrates the pathway that links emissions of greenhouse gases to changes in climate and impacts on human activities and ecosystems:

- Human activities give rise to a sustained pulse of emissions into the atmosphere.
- Not all of these emissions remain in the atmosphere – ultimate atmospheric concentrations of GHGs depend on the action of sinks in removing gases as well as reactions amongst gases in the atmosphere.
- At different time scales, these emissions have different relative warming or cooling impacts (e.g. radiative forcing) on the atmosphere according to the nature of the compound emitted and

its chemical and physical interactions within the atmosphere. For some compounds, the location of emissions matters.

- Numerous climate models indicate that changes in global average atmospheric temperatures lead to changes in the amount and pattern of precipitation, changes in wind patterns and strength, changes in soil moisture, changes in the frequency and strength of extreme weather and changes in sea level.
- These changes in turn may affect terrestrial systems as well as human settlements, activities and energy needs. Potential impacts range from changes in yields and spatial distribution of ecosystems, and agricultural and forest systems to losses of key ecosystems, changes in water resources, and changes in energy needs for heating and cooling.

Transport infrastructure, networks and services are placed at risk from the damaging impact of extreme weather and temperatures as well as rising sea levels. The pattern and distribution of transport demand may also shift alongside climate-impacted human activities placing new demands for infrastructure and posing the risk of stranded assets and capacity where demand falls off of projected levels.

Figure 1.1. **Anthropogenic climate change impact pathway**

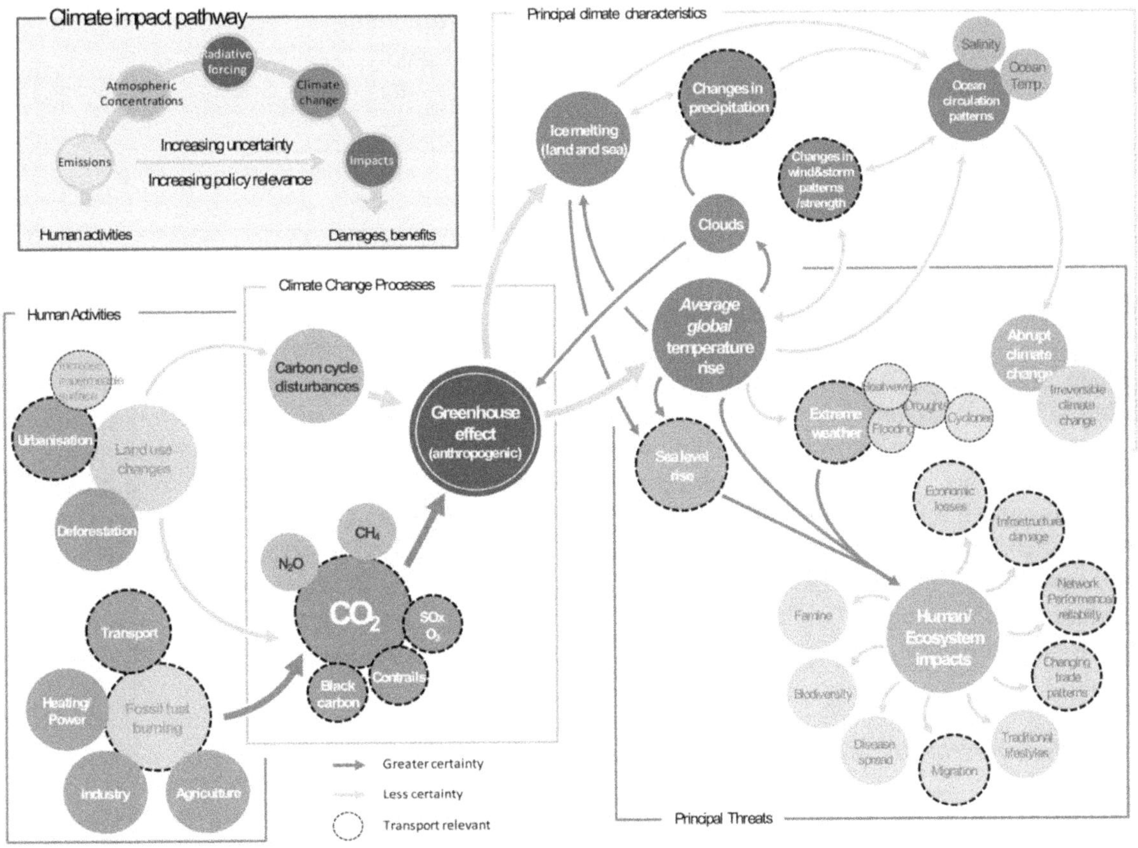

Source: Adapted from UNEP-GRIDA, and den Elzen et al. (2005).

Crucially from the perspective of policy-making, this impact chain is characterised by increasing scientific uncertainty even as policy relevance increases (e.g. towards a quantified estimate of damages that could help to guide policy action). Despite improvements in the scientific understanding of the impact pathway, climate policy making is still characterised by the need to balance significant yet uncertain risks with immediate and consequent actions.

The global and regional climate is already changing in perceptible and measurable ways. The following sections first summarise the current state of understanding of observed changes in the climate system largely based on the report "Climate Change 2013: The Physical Science Basis" (IPCC, 2013). We then examine the state of knowledge about future climate conditions and discuss the use of this knowledge in formulating adaptation policies.

Box 1.2. **Characterising likelihood terms used in the IPCC Fifth Assessment Report**

The IPCC has adopted a carefully calibrated set of terms to characterise both agreement as well as confidence in scientific findings emerging from its Fifth Assessment Report. These are adopted in this section and should guide the reader in understanding these findings.

Virtually certain	**99-100% probability**
Very likely	90-100% probability
Likely	66-100% probability
About as likely as not	33-66% probability
Unlikely	0-33% probability
Very unlikely	0-10% probability
Exceptionally unlikely	0-1% probability

Source: IPCC, 2013.

Observed changes in the climate system

There are centuries (millennia) of observations of critical climate variables that have helped to characterise historic climate periods. These have only become systemic and more-or-less harmonised in the past century and even more so now that global ground-station monitoring has been supplemented by satellite observations.[2] The next few sections present current understanding of the historic climate trends for some transport infrastructure-relevant variables, discussing the evolution of averages as well as extremes, where relevant. Almost all of these phenomena are linked to generalised trends in atmospheric temperatures. These temperatures are changing and the evolution of atmospheric mean and extreme temperatures indicates both a rightward shift and a spreading of the distribution. This suggests more elevated temperatures on average, more frequent unusually warm days and less frequent unusually cold days (Figure 1.2).

Atmospheric temperature: Mean temperature

Why is mean atmospheric temperature relevant for transport infrastructure owners and network managers?

Atmospheric temperature is a fundamental climate variable for infrastructure since temperature means, distribution and extremes must be accounted for in infrastructure design and operational planning. Temperature is a key driver of other climate parameters as well. For instance, a warmer atmosphere holds more moisture and this, combined with differences in temperature (spatial or vertical differences in temperatures or temperature differences between air and sea generate atmospheric fluxes), is the fundamental driver of cloudiness, storminess and precipitation. Atmospheric temperature has an impact on the formation or melting of land and sea ice (including permafrost) and can contribute to thermal expansion of seawater. In the latter case and when land-ice melts, sea levels rise putting transport infrastructure and activity in danger, especially in the context of increased storm strength and frequency due to the damaging effect of storm surges. Increases in atmospheric mean temperature, when combined with elevated CO_2 levels in the atmosphere, lead to accelerated carbonation rates of concrete materials, contributing to accelerated degradation and loss of cohesion and strength. Elevated air temperatures in polluted areas will lead to increased peak levels of ozone and fine particulate matter due to atmospheric chemical feedback cycles.

What is the evidence regarding mean atmospheric temperature trends?

There is evidence of a robust and global warming trend over the period for which there are reliable global data sets. This warming is not uniform nor is the rate of warming steady, especially when considering averages of shorter year ranges. The record shows periods displaying a strong warming trend alternating with periods where the rate of warming has slowed. Recent data suggests that in the current period is displaying lower-than-average rates of warming. Nonetheless, decadal temperature data shows a consistent and increasing trend (Figure 1.3).

According to IPCC (2013), the globally averaged mean land and sea temperature has increased by 0.89°C from 1901 to 2012 (linear trend calculation using multiple independently produced datasets). There is 90% certainty that the temperature change over the period falls between +0.69°C and +1.08°C (90% certainty intervals will be expressed in brackets in the text that follows). The rise in temperature has been 0.72°C [+0.49°C to +0.89°C] from 1951 to 2012 (IPCC, 2013).

Gridded data for the period 1901 to 2012 indicate that the warming trend covers all regions though the Northern Hemisphere; the Arctic regions in particular display the strongest warming. Warming was not uniform across the atmospheric column either with the lower troposphere (0 to 10 kilometre [km] in altitude) warming since 1958 (the year where reliable global data became available) and the lower stratosphere generally cooling over the same period. The direction and patterns of temperature change in the lower troposphere and stratosphere were not spatially consistent with some regions displaying temperatures counter to global trends in both layers (AMS, 2013).

The IPCC notes that each of the last three decades has been successively warmer than any preceding decade since 1850 and that the thirty-year period from 1983 to 2012 was likely (66% to 100% likelihood) to be the warmest in the past 1 400 years. Global average land and sea temperature in 2012 was above the 1981-2010 average and was among one of the ten warmest years over the 1880-2012 period.

Annual temperature averages and decadal averages display significant variability. Trend analysis is also sensitive to starting and ending values as these may express exceptional values that may bias analysis. Short intervals are especially subject to non-representativeness due to natural variability and sensitivity to starting and ending values. Especially problematic are intervals starting or ending during the El Niño or La Niña Southern Oscillation events which result in unusual temperature records (as well as non-typical precipitation patterns and intensity). Isolating the impact of natural variability and identifying robust trends requires long record intervals (at least more than 30 years).

The trend of annual temperature anomalies from the 1961-1990 mean temperature displayed in Figure 1.2 illustrates the above-mentioned variability. This variability may be smoothed by averaging data in "binned" year ranges (e.g. 30, 20, 10 or 5-year "bins"), or by calculating *x*-year moving averages. Care should be made to understand the internal distribution of yearly average temperatures within a "bin" (e.g. what was the standard deviation of temperatures within the interval and what were the deviations from the mean for each year within the interval?) when using "binned" data to estimate a point measurement (e.g. was this decade substantially warmer or cooler than the previous decade?). Running averages can also help smooth some of the natural variability – shorter averaging periods have the advantage of being able to pick up recent changes but also run the risk of over-emphasising changes due to natural variability. Figure 1.3 also displays the 5-year running average of recorded temperature anomalies from the 1961-1990.

Figure 1.2. **Atmospheric temperature: Implications of changing mean values and their distribution**

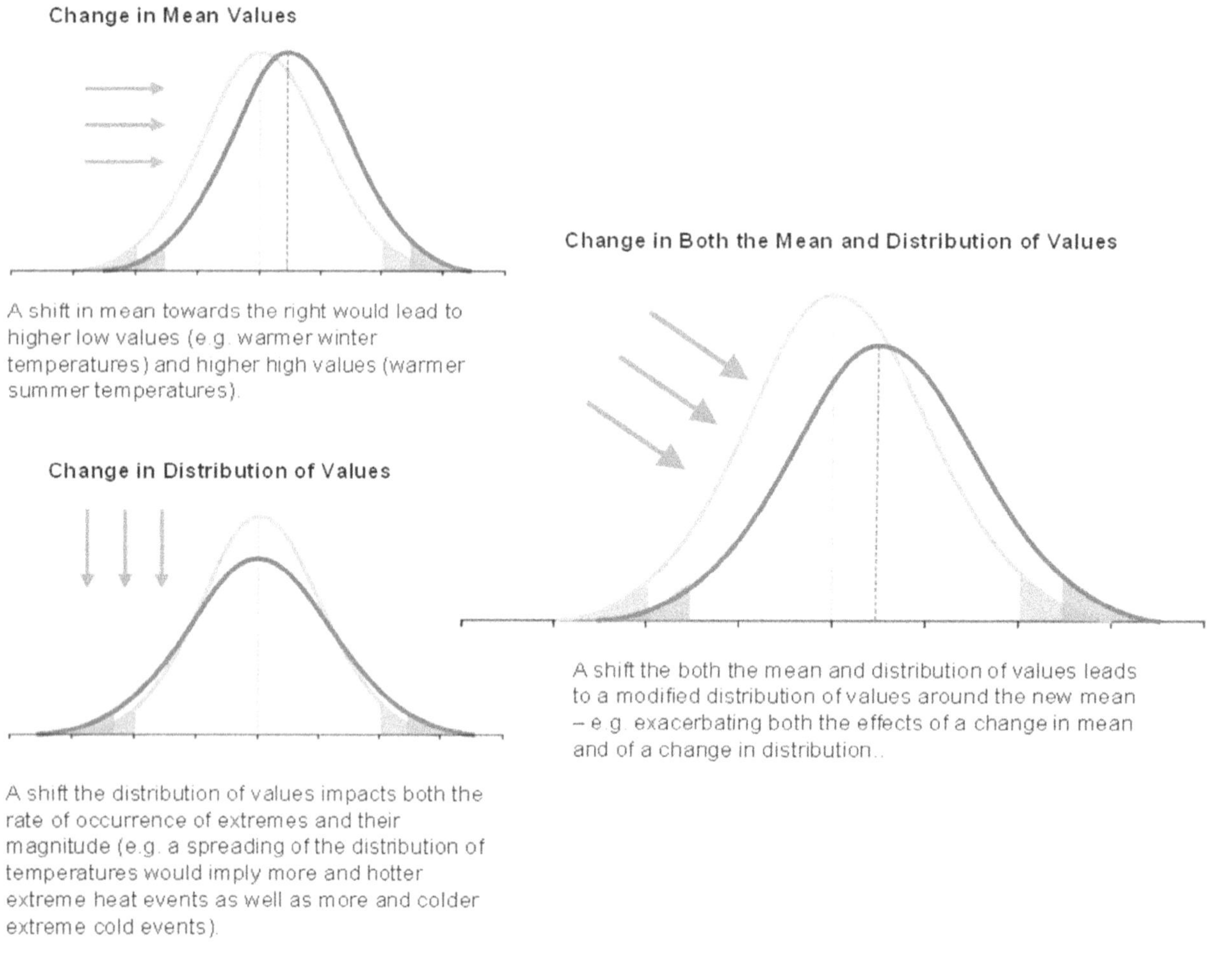

Source: Adapted from IPCC (2013).

temperatures are near 0°C. Regional variation exists due to localised climate interactions – e.g. lake-effect snow has increased in the area east of the North American Great Lakes.

As temperatures warm, atmospheric water vapour levels increase as well by 7% for every degree Celsius. In keeping with observed increases in globally averaged atmospheric temperatures, IPCC (2013) finds that ambient humidity levels have very likely increased since the 1970s near the surface and in the troposphere.

Precipitation: Extreme

Why are precipitation extremes relevant for transport infrastructure owners and network managers?

Extreme precipitation leads to heightened stream and river flow, increased soil runoff as well as flooding. Extreme (or unusually prolonged) precipitation can also lead to a loss of soil cohesion and result in land and mudslides. These hydraulic hazards are among the most damaging for transportation assets and can lead to significant asset damage and sudden failure which interrupt, sometimes significantly so, transport networks.

What is the evidence regarding extreme precipitation trends?

IPCC (2013) notes regional variability in both extreme precipitation and confidence in trend observation. Nonetheless, there have been statistically significant increases in heavy precipitation events in more regions than there have been statistically significant decreases. This holds despite difficulty in establishing a harmonised definition of what constitutes an extreme precipitation event.

Establishing a harmonised global definition of extreme precipitation is difficult given variation in regional climates. Deviation from mean precipitation patterns and intensity is linked to a shift in the mean as well as a possible spread of the distribution of precipitation events. It may also be that many highly-localised extreme precipitation events (e.g. stormbursts) occur at a scale that cannot be captured by current observation systems. Nonetheless, IPCC (2013) finds that more regions have experienced a statistically significant *increase* in extreme precipitation events than have experienced a statistically significant *decrease* in extreme precipitation events. Evidence supporting increased extreme precipitation events is most consistent in central North America and Europe. Findings for winter extreme precipitation events are more consistent than for summer events where seasonal effects have been assessed.

Extreme storms

Why are extreme storms relevant for transport infrastructure owners and network managers?

Extreme storms are accompanied by high winds, extreme precipitation, storm surges in coastal areas, lightning and increased wave energy and amplitude. Cyclones and hurricanes are among the most damaging storm phenomena known but more localised thunderstorms can also result in asset damage and network interruption.

What is the evidence regarding trends in extreme storminess?

IPCC (2013) finds that there is low confidence that tropical storms have increased in number over the last century but that it is virtually certain that extreme storms have become more frequent and that their intensity has increased in the North Atlantic Basin. No significant trend has been observed in thunderstorms and hail.

Large-scale tropical and extra-tropical storms are especially damaging for transport networks. Evidence reviewed in IPCC (2013) does not reveal a statistically significant increase in the frequency of these storm events. However, there is robust regional evidence indicating that the frequency of exceptionally strong storms has increased in the North Atlantic Basin, especially since the early 1970s. There is disagreement on the causes of this trend and whether or not it is a durable one. Evidence from other basins fails to discern significant trends neither in storm frequency nor in extreme storm frequency.

Many smaller-scale extreme storms and related phenomena such as hail and lightening also can disrupt transport activity and networks. These events are much more frequent than large-scale storms but observation networks are often too coarse to adequately record these. With this caveat in mind, IPCC (2013) finds low confidence in the trend of localised extreme storms.

Cryosphere

Why is the state of the cryosphere (snow, river and lake ice, sea ice, glaciers, ice shelves, ice sheets and frozen ground) relevant for transport infrastructure owners and network managers?

The cryosphere is especially sensitive to increases in both average and extreme temperature extremes. Warming trends, and especially winter and polar warming trends, lead to accelerated melting, runoff and frozen soil dynamics. These changes impact transport networks and assets in numerous ways. Shortened snow and ice seasons can lead to a decrease in snow and ice removal costs and snow/ice-related crashes. Less river and lake ice and shorter periods of freezing can increase the accessibility and productivity of inland waterways. Conversely shorter ice seasons cut the period of use of locally important river and lake ice roads in the upper Northern Hemisphere.

Reduced sea ice, and less Arctic ice cover in particular, can potentially open new northern sea routes. At the same time, loss of Arctic sea ice increases heat absorption by the Arctic Ocean and contributes to increased convective fluxes and extreme storminess.

Seasonal melting of frozen soils (permafrost) can lead to loss of slope cohesion and result in landslides in alpine environments. Permafrost instability can lead to soil upheaval which can have a widespread damaging effect for roads, pipelines, railroads and airfields. Indirectly, large-scale melting of land ice contributes to an increase in global sea levels which also jeopardises coastal infrastructure.

What is the evidence regarding changes in the cryosphere?

IPCC (2013) finds that the cryosphere is undergoing major changes. Northern Hemisphere snow cover has decreased, river and lake ice is decreasing and seasonal coverage is shortening, permafrost temperatures and dynamics are increasing, glaciers are shrinking, the Greenland ice sheet is melting and retreating, annual and permanent Arctic ice cover is decreasing (Figure 1.4).

Figure 1.4. **September Arctic Sea ice extent 1980-2015**

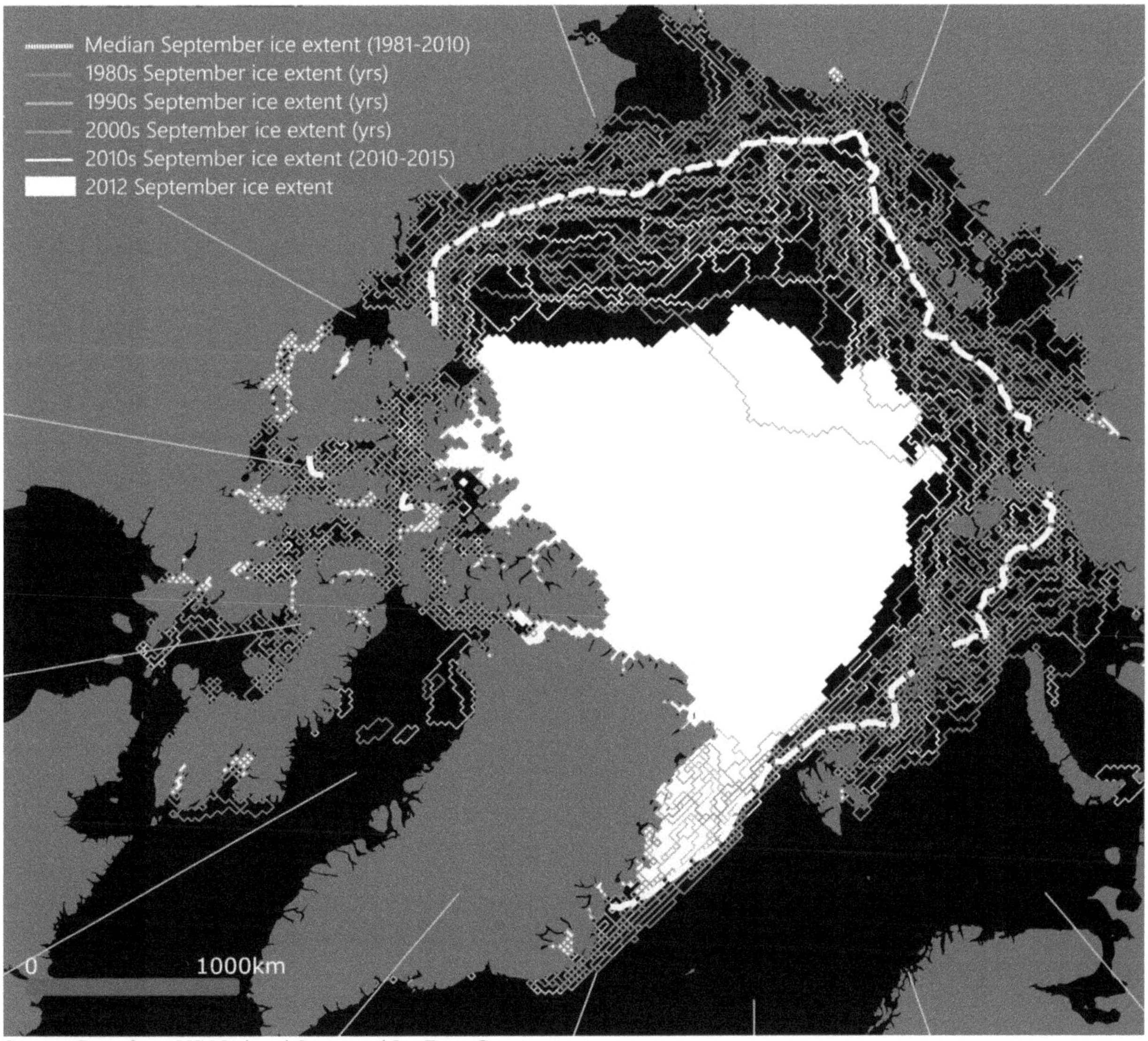

Source: Data from US National Snow and Ice Data Center.

The cryosphere refers to terrestrial components that contain a significant share of frozen water – these include snow cover, lake and river ice, glaciers, ice sheets and shelves, sea ice, ice caps and frozen ground (permafrost). These elements can be transient in nature such as seasonal snow and ice cover or longer-lasting (glaciers, ice sheets, etc.). Their distribution varies but they generally increase in prevalence away from the equator and in altitude. They comprise defining elements of polar regions. Because of their nature, they are sensitive to a rise in global and more localised warming. IPCC (2013) finds broad evidence of significant perturbations to most elements of the cryosphere.

According to the evidence reviewed by the IPCC, Arctic sea ice cover has very likely decreased by 3.1% to 4.1% per decade from 1979 to 2012. The summer minimum Arctic ice cover has decreased at a higher rate of approximately 11.5% per decade over the same period. Average winter Arctic ice thickness has decreased between 1980 and 2008. Antarctic sea ice, on the other hand, has very likely increased by 1.2 to 1.8% per decade from 1979-2012.

Glaciers worldwide have shrunk and lost mass. This loss has very likely led to an increase in sea level of 0.62 ± 0.37 mm yr^{-1} from 1971 to 2009 and this increase has accelerated in recent years accompanying higher rates of ice loss (IPCC, 2013). Momentum in glacial systems means that glaciers will continue to lose mass in the future even if temperatures stabilise.

IPCC (2013) notes with high confidence that the Greenland ice sheet has lost mass over the past twenty years and that this loss has accelerated in recent years. This loss has very likely led to a sea level increase of 0.09 [–0.02 to 0.20] mm yr^{-1} from 1992 to 2001 to 0.59 [0.43 to 0.76] mm yr^{-1} from 2002-2011. The Antarctic ice sheet has similarly lost mass over the past two decades and this loss has also accelerated in recent years. It is likely that Antarctic ice loss has led to an increase in global sea level of 0.08 [–0.10 to 0.27] mm yr^{-1} from 1992–2001, to 0.40 [0.20 to 0.61] mm $yr^{-1}$from 2002-2011.

Where it is well-monitored in the Northern Hemisphere, the seasonal extent of snow cover has decreased over the past twenty years with very high confidence, especially in the spring. IPCC (2013) also finds that Northern Hemisphere winter ice cover of freshwater bodies has also generally decreased in spring. Freeze-up of freshwater bodies has generally occurred later and later with breakup of frozen freshwater bodies occurring sooner and sooner.

Evidence regarding changes in permafrost indicates that frozen soil temperatures have increased in most concerned regions since the 1980s. The rate and depth of seasonal and permanent warming varies according to region with significant warming and permafrost degradation taking place in the Siberia. Findings regarding the depth of the active layer (the layer exposed to seasonal freeze-thaw cycles) vary by region as well and in many areas, active layer depth has increased by a few centimetres to tens of centimetres on average.

Atmospheric and oceanic CO_2 concentration

Why are atmospheric and oceanic CO_2 levels relevant for transport infrastructure owners and network managers?

Alongside other greenhouse gases, atmospheric concentration of CO_2 drives global warming. However, atmospheric concentrations of CO_2 also contribute to chemical reactions that can degrade the coherence and strength of cementitious materials and of concrete in particular. CO_2 absorbed by oceans decreases their pH, increases acidification, which can also contribute to the accelerated degradation of cementitious coastal infrastructure. Climate change impacts stemming from atmospheric concentrations of CO_2 are indifferent to the point of emission but this is not the case for the corrosive impact of CO_2 on vulnerable materials. In particular, increased concentrations of CO_2 in urban areas multiply the corrosive impact of this gas on vulnerable infrastructure elements (Stewart, Wang and Nguyen, 2011).

What is the evidence regarding changes in CO_2 concentrations?

It is certain that atmospheric concentrations of CO_2 have risen since the onset of industrialisation. Atmospheric CO_2 levels were 390.5 ppm in 2011 representing a 40% increase over concentrations in 1750 (IPCC, 2013). Concentrations have likely increased disproportionately in urban areas alongside increases in fossil fuel combustion (Peng and Stewart, 2014). Oceans are also absorbing more CO_2 as atmospheric concentrations of CO_2 rise (Raven et al., 2005).

Future climate projections: Modelling, predicting and describing future climate

Climate change is not new and there are historic periods where changes in prevailing climate have led to unanticipated changes in the scope and strength of weather phenomena that have disrupted, sometimes severely, human activities and infrastructure networks. Generally, however, these changes have not operated on a global scale and have not presented such a wide range of potentially disrupting impacts as have been documented in the previous section. At present, it seems clear that the historical climate record can no longer adequately guide the understanding of the likely future weather conditions, especially past 2050.

If accurately measuring historic and present climate trends is an inherently difficult task, predicting future climate trends is even more challenging and uncertain. From a practical perspective, it is impossible at present (and for the foreseeable future) to predict specific weather phenomena beyond relatively short time frames. This of course would be the most useful information for infrastructure managers to have since it is weather phenomena, and not climate, which are directly responsible for infrastructure damage and failure and ensuing service perturbations. The averaged historic record of weather phenomena instructs this report's understanding of the present climate and gives infrastructure designers and managers a good understanding of the range of climate stressors they will have to account for as well as an idea of the scale and scope of the extreme weather incidents they will face. Traditionally this type of information has been collected by meteorological agencies and provided either directly to engineers or embedded in infrastructure design standards. Historical meteorological data is also used by insurance companies to calculate risk exposure and to set premiums. Since this data is at best an imperfect and worsening predictor of future climate (and at worst, largely irrelevant to describing future climate), planners and engineers must turn to alternative sources of data to guide their designs and investments.

One approach is to look to at other regions of the world that have climate patterns that are analogous to those which are emerging at present. Using such a "climate analogue" approach, planners and engineers witnessing an upwards shift in temperature might look to warmer regions as a way of capturing the range of future climate parameters. Likewise those seeing an increase in atmospheric moisture and wet (e.g. not frozen) precipitation might look to more humid climes for guidance on possible future climate phenomena. The difficulty with this approach is twofold. The first is that there is little statistical certainty that an evolving climate will match that found in a putative "climate analogue". The second is that many transportation assets are longed lived and that under an evolving climate regime, a particular zone might pass through several climate analogue zones (Hallegatte, 2009). At some point in the future, the climate in Barcelona may ultimately become more analogous to that of Casablanca. In that illustrative case, building infrastructure adapted to Casablanca vs. Barcelona is not inherently more difficult. Building long-lived infrastructure capable of handling the both the climate of Barcelona and Casablanca (and points between) is a much more challenging and potentially expensive proposition.

Another option is to look to model outputs regarding future climate variables and use these to guide infrastructure planning, design and investment decisions. Multiple Atmosphere-ocean general circulation models (AOGCMs) that capture interactions between atmospheric composition, radiative forcing and ocean circulation have been developed and are used in co-ordinated manner to simulate future climate conditions. More recently, state-of-the-art Earth System Models (ESMs) extend the modelling environment of AOGCMs to include representations of certain biogeochemical cycles such as the carbon and sulphur cycles and ozone. These model families divide the world into grids (and sometimes stratify these grids vertically into the atmosphere and ocean) at various spatial scales ranging from hundreds of kilometres across to tens of kilometres across. For each cell, the models simulate future climate parameters (e.g. temperature, humidity, and precipitation) after iterative runs that capture inter-cell interactions.

These models must allow scientists to approximate the natural variability of climate systems in order to isolate those climate variables that are evolving out of the historic norm. This is done by running single models multiple times, sometimes with different starting conditions ("ensemble" runs), and averaging the results. Different models are used with their own ensemble runs and the outputs of these are averaged across models. Nonetheless, AOGCM/EOMs models have difficulty in capturing the full extent of natural climate variability, especially for poorly understood phenomena that operate on daily, monthly, annual or decadal time scales. A good example is the challenge of accounting for the effects of the highly disruptive El Niño Southern Ocean Oscillation (ENSO) or its counterpart La Niña. As with other cyclical but poorly understood drivers of regional climate, current global climate model frameworks cannot provide clear guidance on the evolution of these in both frequency and strength as the global climate evolves (Meyer et al., 2014).

Global climate models are complex, computationally demanding, subject to inherent limitations and sometimes compound biases or errors. In particular, they are sensitive to a number of factors that include (Dessai et al., 2009; IPCC, 2013):

- inaccurate specification of climate mechanisms (e.g. lack of scientific understanding or uncertainty in process representation)
- inherent randomness (e.g. stemming from cloud physics)
- error propagation
- uncertainty in observational data
- sensitivity to model resolution
- uncertainty regarding human actions that impact climate (e.g. actions leading to emissions and/or having an impact on sinks).

Because of these limitations, it may very well be that models may produce consistent findings and yet still have low skill in describing the future climate. Model outputs may agree and yet still be in error (Power et al., 2012). Furthermore, while many models display skill at replicating past climate regimes (and thus seem to adequately capture climate dynamics), no scientific assessment can be made as to their ability to capture future climate regimes. In some cases the impact of these limitations can be quantified but in many cases they simply cannot. This results in "some level of irreducible ignorance in our understanding of future climate" (Dessai et al., 2009).

Temperature, humidity and precipitation outputs expressed in absolute terms are generally not a good basis on which to predict future climate. A better approach is to take the relative changes in these three (or other) variables and apply these to observed climate data in order to create climate change scenarios. This allows for the correction of the bias inherent in the simulated and observed climates (Fordham et al., 2011).

From a transport policy perspective, one clear limitation in the current generation of AOGCMs and ESMs is the spatial mismatch between model outputs and relevant spatial scales for asset planning and design purposes. Data regarding general climate parameters in a 100 km by 100 km cell, or even a 30 km by 30 km cell is simply not fine enough for assessing the risk posed by many specific weather phenomena (e.g. thunderstorms, extreme precipitation, flash floods) under an evolving climate.

Various downscaling techniques and regional models can and have been used to deliver more policy-relevant climate data for regional and local applications but these inherit many of the limitations of AOGCMs and ESMs (especially when regional or downscaled models use global model inputs). Compared to the coarse grid of many global climate models, downscaled outputs seem more suited to local infrastructure design and planning uses (see Figure 1.5). However, downscaling may compound limitations inherent to the original model output and is dependent on the continued validity of linkages between local scale and global scale climate variables. Under a changing climate, it is not certain that these linkages will remain constant, or at least remain roughly similar, to what has been observed in the past. More importantly, climate data resulting from global, regional and/or downscaled models may seem analogous to historic climate data. They are not the same and model-based data should not simply be used to replace historic meteorological data by asset planners, designer and managers.

Fundamentally, while regionalisation and downscaling can provide more precision to model outputs, at present these techniques cannot and do not provide more accuracy (Meyer et al., 2014). What these models *do* provide is a range of plausible future climate scenarios that could emerge given the report's present understanding of climate mechanisms and the inherent and sometimes deep uncertainty embedded in the Earth's climate system.

Despite the inherent limitations to the modelling approach and the degree of deep uncertainty that accompanies model outputs, the current generation of ESMs and AOGCMs, and the co-ordinated modelling efforts built around them, are at present the best available source of insight into future climate (IPCC, 2013). Climate models are continually improving, their skill at replicating many historical climate regimes is increasing and they are able to capture many more dynamic elements in the Earth climate mechanism. With the caveats outlined above, they can be used to guide policy – but not necessarily to optimise asset design for one particular climate future.

Figure 1.5. **Spatial grid coverage: Global climate model output vs. downscaled output**

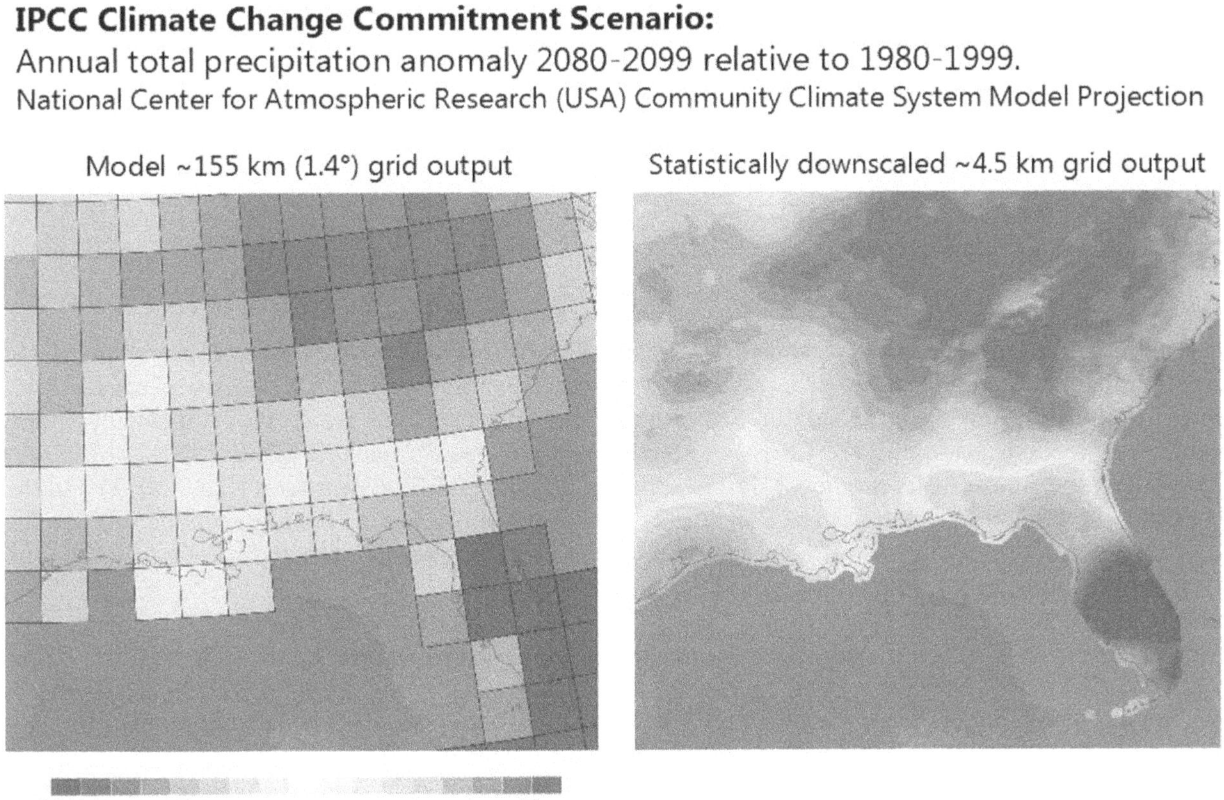

Source: Data from National Center for Atmospheric Research.

Global climate models use scenarios to model the pathway linking human activities, emissions, atmospheric concentrations, radiative forcing (warming/cooling) and ultimately climate impacts.

According to the IPCC, the goal of using scenarios "is not to predict the future but to better understand uncertainties and alternative futures, in order to consider how robust different decisions or options may be under a wide range of possible futures" (IPCC, 2014). In the last two reports prior to the current Fifth IPCC Assessment Report, global climate models used a set of five socio-economic scenarios for population, energy use, industrial development and agricultural activity that were developed in 2000 – the Special Report on Emission Scenarios (SRES) (Nakicenovic et al., 2000). These are now replaced in the most recent Fifth Assessment Report of the IPCC by four so-called "Representative Concentration Pathways" (RCPs) that are conceptually different than the SRES scenarios.

The four RCP scenarios represent different levels or targets for radiative forcing (signalled by the scenario number) and each is associated with an indicative atmospheric concentration of greenhouse gasses that would result in each level of radiative forcing (see Table 1.1). The key difference between the RCP scenarios and the SRES scenarios that preceded them is that there are multiple potential socio-economic scenarios that can lead to each RCP scenario end-point whereas each SRES scenario embodied only one specific socio-economic scenario. This means that socio-economic trajectories can be much more realistically and flexibly addressed in the RCP approach and in particular, adaptation decisions can become a component of the scenario modelling exercise.

Table 1.1. **Atmospheric concentration of greenhouse gases and radiative forcing of each IPCC representative concentration pathway (RCP) scenario**

RCP scenario	Radiative forcing 2100 compared to pre-industrial values (W/m^2)	Atmospheric concentration of GHG, CO_2 equivalent (ppm)
Current situation (2011)		*390.5*
RCP 2.6	+2.6	453
RCP 4.5	+4.5	586
RCP 6	+6	779
RCP 8.5	+8.5	1396

Source: IPCC, 2013.

The modelling framework and scenarios described above are used by the scientific community to project future climate conditions. Crucially, however, these scenarios have no likelihoods associated with them – at this time no basis exists for determining if one scenario is more likely than any other. Therefore projections made in IPCC (2013) are conditioned to specific scenarios. IPCC (2013) discusses these projections on two different timescales. The first is comprised of the near term (2016-2035) and the second for the mid to long term (from 2035 to 2100 and beyond). The following sections discuss the main findings emerging from the Fifth Assessment Report regarding future climate for each of these time scales and for transport-relevant climate variables.

How might climate-related variables evolve in the near-term future?

One important finding from the IPCC's Fifth Assessment Report is that the sensitivity of near-term climate projections to different scenario specifications (in this case the four RCP scenarios) is relatively low. This means that through 2035, the four different RCP scenarios give rise to broadly similar patterns and magnitudes of climate change (IPCC, 2013). This is important for asset owners and transport network managers to understand since it means that range of modelled near-term climate impacts are similar across the range of scenarios. This inherently qualifies some of the deep uncertainty faced by asset owners and network managers since even if probabilities cannot be ascribed to near-term climate outcomes, they are at least similar in scope.

Another finding relates to some of the uncertainties that have not been or at least only partially addressed in the near-term projections – notably the impact of aerosols and uncertainty regarding methane emissions from human activities and land cover change. In the former case, efforts to reduce local air pollution could have a near-term but uncertain cooling impact. In the latter case, including non-natural methane emissions results in a spread of CO_2 equivalent concentrations that is 30% wider than those characterised by the RCP scenarios.

Generally, however, there is higher confidence in some trends than for others. Higher confidence exists (in roughly descending order) for projections regarding global mean temperature and extreme temperatures, surface ocean temperature, sea level rise, permafrost melting and loss of sea and land ice since these stem from well-understood mechanisms that are more readily modelled using the current generation of AOGCMs and ESMs. Less confidence generally exists for projections regarding mean and extreme precipitation as well as large and small-scale storminess. This matters for asset managers and network managers since it is these types of climate-related phenomena that can be most damaging to transport infrastructure.

Near-term trends: Global mean surface temperature

IPCC (2013) projects that globally averaged mean surface air temperatures will likely increase by 0.3°C to 0.7°C by 2035. This finding is sensitive to potential major climate-altering volcanic or solar activity but the impacts of these potential events is considered to be small when compared to radiative forcing brought on by rising greenhouse gas concentrations. Though model runs for all RCP scenarios project increasing temperatures through 2050, the rate of projected warming differs among model runs and between scenarios and the spread between projections increase over time. The indicative likely range of mean temperatures for all RCPs lies in the lower half of the range of all 299 model ensembles (Figure 1.6) but this is conditioned by a number of uncertainties outlined previously, including the evolution of the current slowdown in the rate of temperature increase experienced over the past few years.

The IPCC Fifth Assessment Report finds that it is more likely than not that the global mean surface air temperature for the period 2016 to 2035 will be more than 1°C over the mean for the period ranging from 1850-1900 and very unlikely that this temperature will be more than 1.5°C over the 1850-1900 mean (IPCC, 2013). It is very likely that the rate of warming will be more rapid over land than over sea and that warming over the Arctic will be disproportionately higher than the global mean.

Near-term trends: Ocean temperature

In the absence of major volcanic eruptions which would otherwise lower atmospheric and surface ocean surface temperatures, the Fifth Assessment Report finds that globally averaged surface and near-surface ocean temperatures for the period 2016 to 2035 will be warmer those averaged from 1986 to 2005. This generalised ocean warming will contribute to thermal expansion of the oceans and rising sea levels.

Near-term trends: Extreme surface temperature

Consistent with the recent observed record, the IPCC Fifth Assessment Report finds likely that most land regions will experience more frequent warm days and nights and fewer cold days and nights by 2035 (IPCC, 2013). Evidence supports that the duration of warm spells will increase. As for mean temperatures, these findings are strongly insensitive to the RCP scenario considered over the near term to 2035. The Fifth Assessment Report finds that regional variations exist in the trend of extreme temperature events. In Europe, extreme daytime summer temperatures are projected to increase significantly faster than daytime mean temperatures. In North America, some evidence suggests that the ratio of extremely hot days to extremely cold days will shift from 2 to 1 in the early 2000s to 20 to 1 by 2050 (IPCC, 2013).

Figure 1.6. **Near-term model-based projections for global mean temperature for all four RCP scenarios including likely annual means**

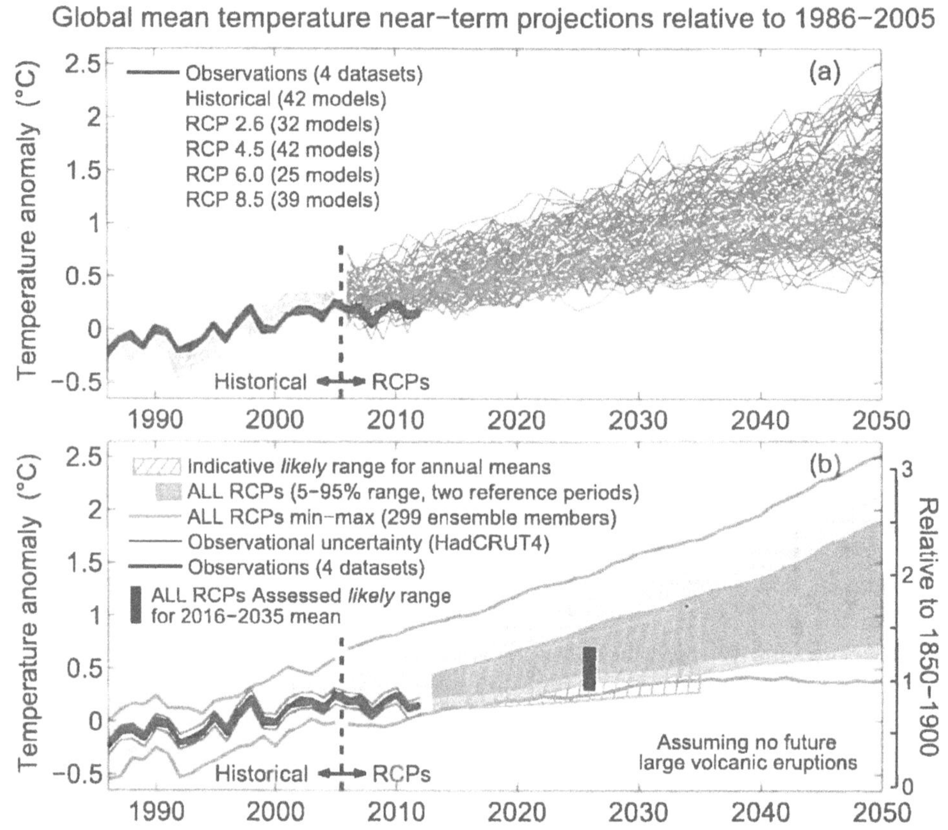

Note: RCP = Representative Concentration Pathway.
Source: Adapted from IPCC, 2013.

Near-term trends: Precipitation

Mean precipitation is very likely to increase in the mid to upper latitudes and in wet regions like the tropics whereas mean precipitation levels are more likely than not to decrease in subtropical zones. Natural regional variability and the emissions of anthropogenic aerosols will have an impact on precipitation. Findings regarding precipitation are more consistent at large scales and less so at smaller scales. Near-surface specific humidity is very likely to increase over land. Generally, and especially at smaller scales and nearer-term periods, the magnitude of projected mean precipitation levels is smaller than the magnitude of natural variability – e.g. there is a low signal-to-noise ratio (IPCC, 2013).

Near-term trends: Extreme precipitation

Evidence reviewed by (IPCC, 2013) confirms a clear upwards trend in the frequency of extreme precipitation events on average but highlights significant regional variations in extreme precipitation patterns in the near-term. These extreme events will increase as atmospheric water vapour content increases in reaction to atmospheric warming. Short-term extreme events like thunderstorms may also increase in frequency and strength but current modelling approaches cannot establish confidence in these localised trends.

Near-term trends: Extreme storms

Due to a range of complicating factors, insufficient data and conflicting projections, IPCC (2013) finds low confidence in regional and global projections of tropical cyclone trends at present. Findings are inconclusive as to whether the frequency of these storms will increase, remain steady or decrease. Likewise, there is also low confidence in near-term tropical storm intensity projections. These findings do not indicate that tropical cyclone frequency and strength will not increase (or decrease) but that there is simply not sufficient confidence in backing either claim.

Near-term trends: Cryosphere

As near-term global mean temperatures rise, it is very likely that observed trends in the cryosphere will continue unabated. This means that it is likely that further shrinking of Arctic sea ice will take place and in some projections may lead to a nearly ice-free summer in the near-term. Further decreases in northern high-latitude springtime snow cover and more dynamic and deep thawing of permafrost soils are also likely. With the decrease in cold extremes and the later onset and earlier breakup onset of frozen conditions, there will likely be a shortening of the ice season for northern latitude rivers and lakes (IPCC, 2013).

How might climate-related variables evolve in the mid- to long-term future?

Projecting the evolution of climate variables past 2035 and to 2100 and beyond necessarily involves increasing uncertainty linked to the model and knowledge-based limitations outlined in the previous section. The accuracy of longer-term model-based projections is inherently unknown at the time of the projection. Given the challenge of correctly capturing the complex phenomena at work in the Earth's climate system and the fact that key uncertainties regarding the mid- to long-term future may be irreducible. This is not to say that there is no value in scenario-based modelling exercises looking at the long-term – there is. For one, there is no better way to try to understand the interplay between emission levels and potential future climate regimes. Modelling allows us to better grasp the relative sensitivity of the climate system and its component elements to emissions and activities. It also allows us to understand the limitations of our knowledge regarding the future and, crucially, areas expected to have no actionable information regarding the evolution of critical climate variables.

The modelling undertaken in support of the IPCC's Fifth Assessment Report indicates that there is broad consistency in projections regarding both the large-scale patterns and magnitude of change. This consistency does not necessarily imply accuracy but it does indicate that the models employed are in agreement about the broad parameters of longer-term future climate change. (IPCC, 2013) notes that model agreement and confidence in projections depends on the variable in question and the level of spatial or temporal averaging. Confidence is generally higher for large-scale mean temperature and precipitation trends as well as sea level projections over longer averaging periods. Confidence is generally lower for other climate-related variables (e.g. extreme precipitation, storminess, etc.) and for smaller-scale spatial extents and shorter averaging periods.

Long-term trends: Mean and extreme global mean surface temperatures

According to IPCC (2013) global mean surface temperatures will continue to increase should greenhouse gas emissions continue to rise. Projected global mean temperature increases are related to the radiative forcing implied in each of the RCP scenarios and are likely to vary from 0.3°C to 1.7°C for

RCP 2.6 to 2.6°C to 4.8°C for RCP 8.5 for the period 2081 to 2100 and in relation to the period 1986-2005. Given the current GHG emissions trajectory and about the current understanding of atmospheric and ocean cycles, this warming trend has significant and durable momentum. The global increase in mean temperatures will not be uniform – more warming will occur over land than over sea and faster warming will likely occur in the Northern Hemisphere[3] and certainly occur in the Arctic. There is evidence linking accelerated Arctic warming to greater instability in Northern Hemisphere atmospheric circulation. So-called "Arctic amplification" effects are linked to the emergence of more extreme and unstable weather patterns in the Northern Hemisphere (Francis and Skific, 2015).

The short-term trend of more frequent and hotter temperature extremes and fewer cold temperature extremes will virtually certainly continue through to the end of the 21st Century (and likely beyond). Twenty-year return values for both hot and cold extremes will increase at rates greater than the respective rates of change for mean summer and winter temperatures. Hot extremes will occur more frequently, last longer and be warmer than in the past (IPCC, 2013). Cold extremes will be less frequent but they may be as cold as or colder still than today's cold extremes, especially in the upper latitudes.

Long-term trends: Ocean temperature

The short- to mid-term warming of the upper layer of the ocean is projected to warm for all four RCP scenarios. Storage of atmospheric heat by the ocean will only slowly dissipate leading to some long-term phenomena like sea level rise. Changes in ocean circulatory patterns brought about by ice melt and thermal changes could have severe and lasting impacts on global climate but current evidence is does not support a sudden or abrupt change of these in the 21st century.

Long-term trends: Global sea level rise

The rate of global sea level rise during the 21st century is very likely to surpass the rate of sea level rise experienced from 1971 to 2010 for all of the four RCP scenarios. This increase is due both to continued thermal expansion of the sea due to the increase in mean global temperature as well as to the melting of land-based glaciers and ice sheets (especially that covering Greenland). IPCC (2013) finds that the likely range of global mean sea level rise will span from an estimated +0.26 to +0.55 metre increase in 2081-2100 compared to 1986-2005 levels (5% and 95% values for all projections) for RCP 2.6 to +0.52 to +0.98 metres for RCP 8.5 (See Figure 1.7). Sea level rise may be higher still but insufficient evidence exists to determine the probability of such an occurrence. Even more so than with the trend in mean temperatures, the oceans' thermal momentum means that this rise is already committed and will virtually certainly continue beyond the 21st century (and possibly for several more centuries). Sustained warming between 2°C and 4°C over pre-industrial global mean temperatures would result in the complete loss of the Greenland ice sheet and a sea level rise of approximately 7 metres over a millennium or more. Crucially, IPCC (2013) notes that abrupt and irreversible sea level rise resulting from warming-related instability of the Antarctic ice sheet is possible but that insufficient information exists to assess this probability.

Figure 1.7. **Historic sea level from tide gauges and projections for RCP 2.6 and RCP 2.8**

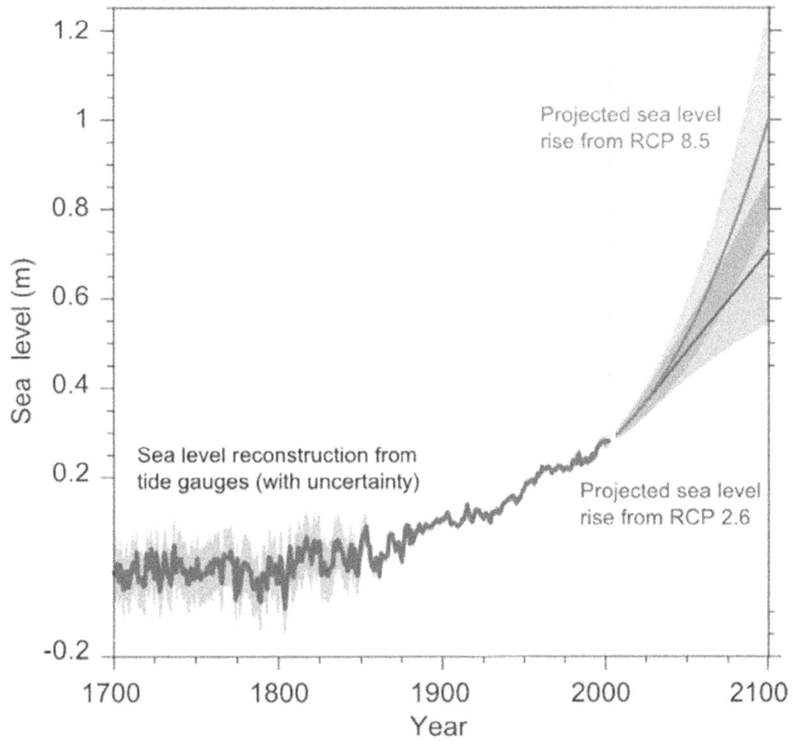

Note: RCP = Representative Concentration Pathway
Source: Adapted from IPCC, 2013.

Long-term trends: Mean and extreme global precipitation

Warming temperatures will increase in the amount of water vapour in the atmosphere and lead to a concomitant increase in the amount of global mean precipitation. The virtually certain increase in global mean precipitation will be uneven however with some regions seeing an increase, some a decrease and some no change at all. Land masses in the Northern Hemisphere, especially at upper latitudes, are likely to experience more precipitation than now. IPCC (2013) finds that conversely, many mid-latitude and subtropical dry regions will see less precipitation than now. Generally, the change in contrast between wet and dry regions and between wet and dry seasons within regions will increase through the 21st century.

The increase in global mean temperatures will likely contribute to more frequent and more extreme short-duration storms. This is especially true for most of the mid-latitude and wet tropical land masses that will very likely see more intense and frequent precipitation events. Even regions that are expected to see less overall precipitation may see more intense and damaging extreme precipitation events (IPCC, 2013). Damage from these events to transport infrastructure in arid areas may be multiplied due to runoff characteristics on very dry soils.

Long-term trends: Cryosphere

Loss of seasonal and perennial Arctic sea ice is very likely to continue through the 21st century leading to a nearly ice-free polar region in RCP 8.5 by 2081-2100. There is evidence suggesting that changes in ocean and atmospheric circulatory regimes induced by the loss of Arctic ice cover will contribute to more frequent and extreme Arctic cyclones (Vavrus, 2013). The Antarctic is also expected to experience a reduction in sea ice extent and volume though there is less confidence in this finding (IPCC, 2013). Northern Hemisphere snow cover is very likely to diminish through to the end of the 21st century. The global extent of permafrost coverage is very likely to retreat and the amplitude of the active layer in permafrost soils is likely to increase.

References

AMS (2013), "State of the Climate in 2012". Bulletin of the American Meteorological Society, August, Vol 94/8.

den Elzen, M. et al., (2005), "Analysing Countries' Contribution to Climate Change: Scientific and Policy-related Choices". *Environmental Science & Policy,* Vol. 8/6.

Dessai, S., R. Lempert and R. Pielke Jr. (2009), "Do we need better predictions to adapt to a changing climate?" *Eos*, Transactions American Geophysical Union, Vol. 9/13.

Fordham, D., T. Wigly and B. Brook (2011), "Multi-model Climate Projections for Biodiversity Risk Assessments". *Cological Applications*, Vol. 21/8.

Francis, J. and N. Skific (2015), "Evidence Linking Rapid Arctic Warming to Mid-latitude Weather Patterns". *Philosophical Transactions A*, Vol. 373, p. 2045.

Hallegatte, S. (2009), "Strategies to Adapt to an Uncertain Climate". *Global Environmental Change*, Vol. 19.

IPCC (Intergovernmental Panel on Climate Change) (2014), Field, C.B V.R. Barros, D.J. Dokken, K.J. Mach, M.D. Mastrandrea, T.E. Bilir, M. Chatterjee, K.L. Ebi, Y.O. Estrada, R.C. Genova, B. Girma, E.S. Kissel, A.N. Levy, S. MacCracken, P.R. Mastrandrea, and L.L. White (eds.). Cambridge University Press, Cambridge, and New York.

IPCC (Intergovernmental Panel on Climate Change) (2013), "Climate Change 2013: The Physical Science Basis" (Summary for Policymakers), Working Group I contribution to the IPCC Fifth Assessment Report, Geneva.

IPCC (Intergovernmental Panel on Climate Change) (2012), "Managing the Risks of Extreme Events and Disasters to Advance Climate Change Adaptation". A Special Report of Working Groups I and II of the Intergovernmental Panel on Climate Change. Field, C.B., V. Barros, T.F. Stocker, D. Qin, D.J. Dokken, K.L. Ebi, M.D. Mastrandrea, K.J. Mach, G.-K. Plattner, S.K. Allen, M. Tignor, and P.M. Midgley (eds.). Cambridge University Press, Cambridge and New York.

Met Office Hadley Centre observations datasets (HadCRUT4), http://www.metoffice.gov.uk/hadobs/hadcrut4/data/current/download.html (accessed 01 October 2013).

Meyer, M. et al. (2014), *Climate Change, Extreme Weather Events and the Highway System: A Practitioner's Guide*, Transportation Research Board of the National Academies, Washington, D.C.

Nakicenovic, N. et al. (2000), *Emission Scenarios: A Special Report of Working Group III of the Intergovernmental Panel on Climate Change*, Cambridge University Press, New York.

National Center for Atmospheric Research, https://ncar.ucar.edu/.

Peng, L. and M. Stewart (2014), "Climate Change and Corrosion Damage Risks for Reinforced Concrete Infrastructure in China". *Structure and Infrastructure Engineering*. Vol. 12/4, pp. 499-516.

Power, S., F. Delage, R. Colman and A. Moise (2012), "Consensus on 21st Century Rainfall Projections in Climate Models More Widespread than Previously Thought". *Journal of Climate*, Vol. 25/11.

Raven, J. et al. (2005), *Ocean acidification due to increasing atmospheric carbon dioxide*. The Royal Society, London.

Ropeik D. and G. Gray (2002), *RISK! A Practical Guide for Deciding What's Really Safe and What's Really Dangerous in the World Around You*, Houghton Mifflin.

Stewart, M. G., X. Wang and M.N. Nguyen (2011), "Climate Change Impact and Risks of Concrete Infrastructure Deterioration". *Engineering Structures*, Vol. 33.

UNEP-GRIDA, The GRID-Arendal Maps & Graphics Library (2013), http://maps.grida.no/go/graphic/climate-change-global-processes-and-effects1 (accessed 30 September 2013).

US National Snow and Ice Data Center, http://nsidc.org/data/seaice_index/ (accessed 29 September 2015).

Vavrus, S. (2013), "Extreme Arctic Cyclones in CMIP5 Historical Simulations". *Geophysical Research Letters*, Vol. 40/23.

Notes

1 The six greenhouse gases tracked under the Kyoto protocol are: Carbon Dioxide (CO_2), Methane (CH_4), Nitrous Oxide (N_2O), Perfluocarbons (PFCs), Hydrofluorocarbons (HFCs) and Sulphur hexafluoride (SF_6). Other greenhouse gases include ozone-depleting substances as well as several other compounds that lead to changes in atmospheric temperatures (see Chapter 2).

2 Even so, there remain sources of uncertainty in the recent historic record spanning from the mid-19th century to present and even in the very recent historic records from the middle of the 20th century on. These uncertainties relate to biases inherent in different datasets, biases inherent from measurement (instruments) and sampling and biases stemming from incomplete coverage.

3 Not all models agree though, with one in particular indicating the potential for cooling across significant portions of the Northern Hemisphere for 2081-2100 (IPCC, 2013).

change. Koetse and Rietveld (2009) point out that climate change could impact the availability or desirability of tourist destinations (e.g. by opening up new opportunities or, conversely, rendering existing tourism destinations unpleasant because of heat or storminess) and could lead to new patterns of agricultural production which could shift certain trade flows away from existing pairs. Besides altering patterns and intensities of human activities over the long run, climate change could also erode the economic viability of certain coastal areas (Hallegate et al., 2013). These changes will have an impact on transport demand and could lead to over- or under-supply of transport infrastructure and related opportunity costs.

Asset life cycle: Maintenance requirements and climate exposure

Transportation infrastructure assets require continuous attention in terms of maintenance, to counter deterioration. Indeed, once new infrastructure has been built, it will need to be operated and maintained throughout its useful life in order to deliver expected benefits. Many road and to a certain extent, rail, airport and waterborne transport asset systems may seem "perpetual" in that they are in the "operate and maintain" part of their life cycle with no expectation of closure, decommissioning, deconstruction or demolition (CIRIA, 2009). It is not uncommon for much of the existing infrastructure stock to have been in service for longer than the current design life of equivalent assets as is the case in the United Kingdom (CIRIA, 2009). Funding of operations and maintenance are a direct result of capital spending decisions and may be expected to extend indefinitely into the future for many assets – maintenance expenditures should be therefore taken into account over an indefinite (life cycle of the infrastructure) timeframe for these assets and asset systems. While the expectation may be that transport services are "perpetual", that is not the case for physical assets and asset subcomponents which have limited lifespans and which will need to be refurbished and/or replaced. This means that assets will be differently exposed to climate change. For some asset components, the risk is minimal since their design life is shorter than the period over which changes in climate may manifest themselves – e.g. in the case of road surfaces. For other asset subcomponents, the risk is significant since their design life (or effective period of use in the case of existing assets) extends well within climate timescales (e.g. 50+ years).

Multiple sub-components

Another point well worth noting is that transport asset systems are in fact a collection of individual, interconnected asset sub-classes that each play a role in delivering expected performance outcomes. For instance, the UK Highways Agency has identified 25 asset components divided into seven asset sub-classes that are critical for the "highway asset" to function properly and meet users' service needs and expectations (Figure 2.1). These asset components all have different lifespans and maintenance/refurbishment schedules that must be adhered to in order to minimise the risk of asset failure and/or service disruption. Assets system components typically outlast political and budgetary cycles and for many longer-life assets, extend into timescales where conditions cannot at this time be accurately predicted (e.g. future demand, climate impacts).

Connected and interdependent systems

Transportation networks are composed of multiple, interconnected infrastructure asset systems. Transport networks also do not operate in isolation to one another nor to other infrastructure networks. They often rely on effective drainage systems and access to continuous power, data and communications services. Robustness and interconnectedness are at the heart of civil engineering and infrastructure design decisions. Engineers must design infrastructure such that it delivers expected services despite being exposed to a wide range stressors, including those linked to weather. They must also design infrastructure systems such that the potential loss of service in one system does not propagate to other systems.

Figure 2.1. **UK Highway Agency Asset System: Component lifespans**

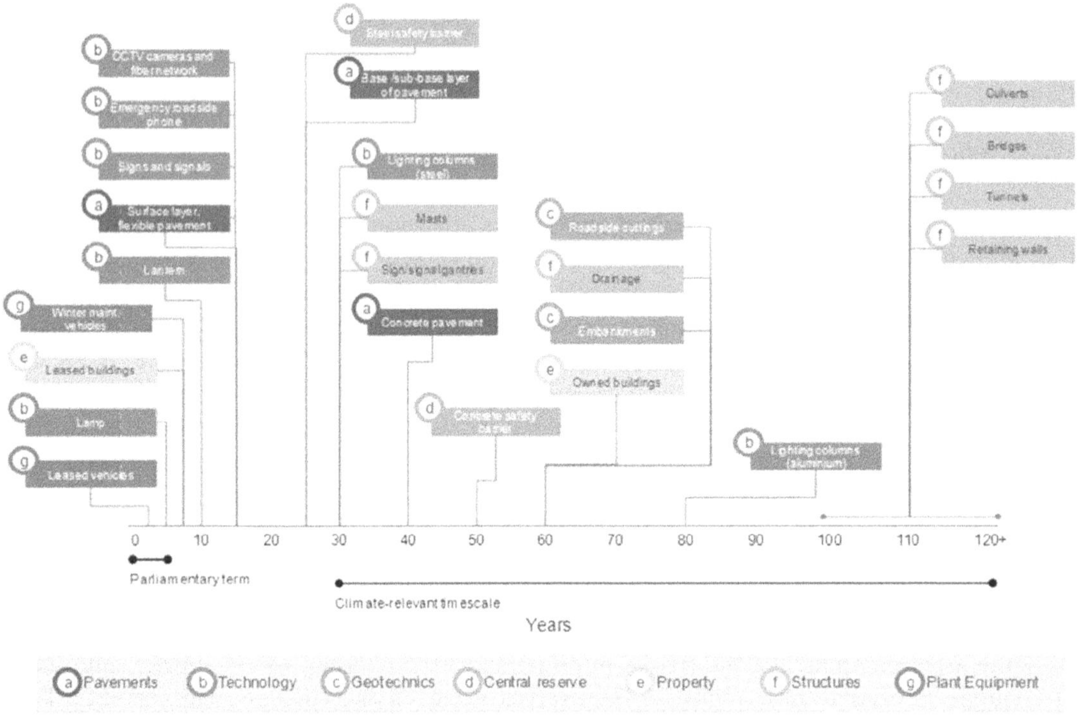

Source: UK Highways Agency, 2011.

Multiple responsibilities

Responsibility for transport infrastructure is not uniform across modes and this will have an impact on the manner in which strategic decisions regarding investment and maintenance are made. The model of ownership and operation will also have an incidence on the choice of risk management and insurance framework adopted. Ports and airports may be owned or operated by the private sector or by public authorities. Rail infrastructure may be owned by one actor and rail services operated by another. Similarly public transport services may be concessioned to private operators or may be the responsibility of local government. Assets owned by the private sector will typically be insured on a market basis while publicly owned assets, and roads in particular, will be self-insured in the sense that damage costs are borne by public authorities.

Local government exposure

Public ownership is generally the norm for road infrastructure but this responsibility is typically split across multiple levels of government. Strategic motorways and major connectors may be under the responsibility of national governments – who may in some cases grant concessions for the operation of these roads to private operators for toll-based operations. These primary roads and motorways carry a significant share of overall traffic. In the UK, the strategic road network represents only 2% of the overall road network length but it carries one-third of all passenger traffic and two-thirds of all freight traffic (DfT, 2013). Nonetheless, despite the disproportionate importance of motorways and major connectors, the overwhelming majority of roads and a significant share of traffic are carried by roads owned and maintained by local and regional authorities. In Australia, for example, the country's 560 local governments own or are responsible for approximately AUS 212 billion worth of assets, in large part comprised of transport and related assets. This responsibility is often not matched with commensurate funding, especially for maintenance. Carter (2013) succinctly notes this tension:

> Local government is asset rich but income poor. The assets include roads, cycle paths, footpaths, water and sewerage networks, levees, dams, stormwater drains...Many of these assets underpin the basic services we take for granted each day. These assets are subliminal in our consciousness until water supply is interrupted, bridges are closed or weight-limited, townships are flooded, or we crash on an unsealed road.

Climate stressors and their impacts on transport infrastructure

Climate "stressors" are those climate variables[1] including temperature (average, extremes and amplitude), humidity, precipitation and wind that either directly or indirectly affect the siting, design, construction, operation or maintenance of transport infrastructure (Meyer et al., 2014). These stressors may be linked to gradual changes in prevailing conditions or may come about suddenly in the context of extreme events.

As noted in Chapter 1, climate change will shift average climate variables as well as the magnitude and severity of natural phenomena. The former includes changes in temperature, precipitation, soil humidity, etc. while the latter include storms, storm surges, flooding (Cochran, 2009). Changes in average values are generally expected to impact infrastructures in the mid and long run, while shifts in the intensity and severity of natural phenomena could already have a direct catastrophic effect on transportation infrastructure today.

Table 2.1. **Climate change stressors: Gradual vs. sudden**

Category	Climate-related stressors
Changes in average values	• Change in average temperature • Change in precipitation • Change in humidity • Sea level rise • Permafrost melting
Changes in the intensity and severity of weather phenomena	• Severe storms • Storm surge • Extreme precipitation • Flooding • Draught • Hurricanes • Heat waves

Source: Compiled from: Larsen et al., 2008; Cochran, 2009; Karl et al. (eds.), 2009; Koetse and Rietveld, 2009; Eichhorst, 2009; Meyer et al, 2011; Inturri and Ignaccolo, 2011; Meyer et al., 2014; Nemry et Demirel, 2012.

For example, increased scouring[2] of bridge abutments could result from a change in longer-term precipitation, runoff and streamflow patterns but this is expected to occur over longer time periods. On the other hand, a severe flood resulting from extreme rainfall or rapid snowmelt could lead a bridge to collapse in a matter of minutes. Such a categorisation is critical for deploying adaptive measures; while catastrophic events require mostly short- and mid-term actions (preparation of emergency response services, infrastructure repair and retrofitting), adaptation to longer-term changes in weather patterns may require design and construction of new transportation infrastructures or re-siting decisions (Cochran, 2009). Typical climate stressors for the two categories are presented in Table 2.1.

What constitutes a climate "stress" is largely tied to the design of infrastructure and the particular intensity of the climate variable. Culverts sized to handle 100 mm of rain in a day may not be affected if 80 mm of rain falls over the course 24 hours. The same culvert may be overly "stressed" and may possibly fail should 80 mm of rain fall in two hours. While specific threshold values for climate stressors are context-specific, there is some value nonetheless in assessing stressor threshold values. Leviäkangas et al. (2012) have estimated rough damage threshold values for extreme weather phenomena (see Table 2.2). These values can serve as guidance for understanding when damaging impacts may emerge during extreme events.

Table 2.2. **Most harmful extreme weather phenomena and their threshold values**

Phenomena	Threshold 1 harmful impacts possible, 0.33	Threshold 2 harmful impacts likely, 0.66	Threshold 3 harmful impacts certain, 0.99
Heat (mean daily temperature)	≥+25°C	≥+32°C	≥+43°C
Cold (mean daily temperature)	<0°C	<-7°C	<-20°C
Rain	≥30 mm/d	≥100 mm/d	≥150 mm/d
Snowfall	≥1 cm/d	≥10 cm/d	≥20 cm/d
Wind (gust speed)	≥17 m/s	≥25 m/s	≥32 m/s

Source: Leviäkangas et al., 2012.

Climate stressors will impact different asset sub-components in different ways. This implies that a transport asset may be affected by a number of climate-related factors, with each factor contributing differently to the degradation of one or more infrastructure elements. This is particularly true for infrastructure comprised of multiple sub-components such as pavements, bridges and tunnels, where changes in weather patterns trigger different deterioration mechanisms.

Climate stressors operate simultaneously or cumulatively thus amplifying their individual impact on infrastructure. For example, the structural integrity of a steel bridge superstructure could be weakened by extreme temperature changes, while higher precipitation will accelerate scouring of its abutments. Ultimately, the bridge may fail due to the cumulative impact of both stressors. In another example, combined hazard-forcing mechanisms, including saturated soils due to increased average precipitation and soil humidity levels, extreme rainfall, and a storm surge, could lead to severe flood damage to roads, bridges and embankments that paralyse transport services. Cumulative climate-impacts don't have to lead to failure for them to temporarily degrade transport system performance. High winds combined with extreme rains may make a bridge unsafe to use and its approaches temporarily impassable but these impediments will recede after the storm event. Whereas each hazard-forcing mechanism on its own may have resulted in manageable impacts, their combination simultaneously or in rapid succession leads to serious or catastrophic results. Table 2.3 reviews the current understanding of the negative and positive impacts of various climate stressors on transport infrastructure.

Table 2.3. **Overview of climate stressor impacts on transport networks**

Climate stressor	Potential transport infrastructure impacts
Warmer summers	Heat-related deterioration of materials, asphalt rutting, rail buckling. Longer airport runway requirements. Loss of inland navigation capacity due to low water levels. Thermal expansion of bridges and joints. Damage to machinery and engine overheating. Heat damage to ITS systems. Wildfire and smoke risk. Reduced construction and maintenance work hours. Soil subsidence due to drought. Accelerated heave and/or loss of cohesion of permafrost soils.
Warmer winters	Reduced ice and snow removal costs. More opportunities for winter-time maintenance and construction. Potential increase in fogginess. Asset deterioration due to more frequent freeze-thaw cycling. More accessible inland waterways. Loss of use of snow and ice roads; increase in permafrost heave. Increased flood risk due to increase in wet winter precipitation.
Changes in soil and air humidity	Decreased soil humidity can lead to subsidence of geotechnical substrata. Increases in soil humidity can lead increased runoff due to saturation, loss of cohesion resulting in structural instability for bridges, sub-bases, slope cuts and embankments or increased landslide risk. Increases in air humidity, in conjunction with heat, can reduce working hours available for construction, operations and maintenance.
Increased precipitation (average and extremes)	Increase in weather-related crashes, traffic disruptions and delays. Flooding of land transport infrastructure, hydraulic damage to bridge abutments and footings, prolonged standing water damage to geotechnical substrata, culvert failures and road, rail washouts. Collapse of embankments, mudslides, landslides and slope failures. Flooding of subways and public transport facilities (e.g. bus depots). Inability for transport workers to get to their work, increased incidence of slushflow avalanches.
Stronger and more frequent extreme winds	Damage to technical superstructure of roads, railroads, port and airports. Damage to lighting, power and communications networks. Traffic disruption and closures due to felled trees. Temporary closures of port and airports and resultant backlogged operations. Storm debris clearance.
Sea level rise and storm surges	Erosion of coastal roads and railroad infrastructure, disruption for transport networks and activities situated in low-lying areas. Higher tides for port facilities and potential disruption of road/rail access to ports. Potential for flooding exacerbated by inadequately dimensioned drainage facilities. Exposure of low-lying coastal airports to storm-surge damage and flooding. More frequent and/or permanent inundation of transport facilities in low-lying areas. Corrosion of steel and concrete materials. Increased scour for defensive structures and bridges.
Change in the frequency of winter storms	Less or more ice or snow for all modes.
Lightening	Disruption of power supply (overhead catenaries, lights, ICT, etc.)

The following sections describe climate-related impacts on the different types of transportation asset systems: roadways, railways, airports, ports and inland waterways. For roadways, this report considers pavements, earthworks, and bridges (including culverts), while for rail it considers tracks, ballast and substructure. For airports this report looks at airport pavements and terminals whereas for ports, it looks at docks, protective elements and sea-side construction. Although this report does not detail them here, both airports and ports include a number of buildings, electrical-mechanical engineering related facilities and machinery (e.g. cranes in ports) that are essential to their functioning; these are noted where appropriate. Each asset type is analysed at the level of separate sub-components where relevant; for example, pavements can be separated into asphalt, base and sub-base layers, while bridges in deck, substructure and superstructure. There are of course common elements – especially as concerns geotechnical substructures. These are examined once and referenced later as necessary.

The following sections discuss change impacts to transportation assets on two levels. The first level refers to the type of infrastructure considered (roadway, railway and so on); appropriate disaggregation is offered on a case-by-case element and component. And the second level refers to the particular climate change parameter considered. Table 2.4 summarises the infrastructure assets examined and their components.

Table 2.4. **Transportation asset types, elements and components**

Asset	Elements	Components (where applicable)
Road	Pavement	Flexible pavements • Asphalt layer • Base • Sub-base • Sub-grade Rigid pavements • Concrete slab • Base • Sub-base • Sub-grade
	Bridge	• Deck • Superstructure • Substructure
	Tunnel	• Lighting • Emergency communications • Monitoring equipment, ventilation equipment
	Earthworks	• Slopes • Embankments
	Drainage	• Culverts
	Signage, power, lighting, ITS and communications	• Signage • Variable messaging signs • Light masts • Embedded sensors • Cameras and monitoring equipment

Table 2.4. **Transportation asset types, elements and components (continued)**

Asset	Elements	Components (where applicable)
Railway	Track	• Rail • Slippers • Joints • Ballast • Switches
	Substructure	• Railbed
	Earthworks	• Same as roadway
	Power and signaling	• Overhead catenaries • Signaling equipment
	Drainage	• Culverts
Airport	Pavement	• Same as roadway
	Earthworks and flood protection	• Dykes and protective walls for coastal and low-lying airports
	Terminals and buildings	• N/A
	Drainage	• Culverts • Pumping equipment (low-lying coastal facilities)
	Equipment	• N/A
Port	Docks and wharfs	• N/A
	Terminals and buildings	• N/A
	Equipment	• Cranes • Mobile cargo handling equipment
Inland waterways		• N/A

Roadway infrastructure

The road network is comprised of strategic, high-volume primary arterials and motorways that carry a substantial amount of traffic and an extensive network of lower-volume secondary access roads that are necessary for door-to-door travel. In nearly all instances the primary networked is paved with asphalt or concrete as is a significant portion of the secondary network though in many remote regions, roads may be gravel-surfaced or even seasonal in nature as is the case with ice-roads in northern latitudes.

As road infrastructures are constantly exposed to weather, their component materials are evidently affected by weather phenomena such as heat, rain, and wind. Furthermore, hazards can have direct impacts on the structural integrity and functionality of road infrastructures. These impacts are multiple, oftentimes simultaneous and can cumulatively lead to unavailability, damage and potential failure – though some climate impacts may be positive. Figure 2.2 outlines the links between climate trends, climate stressors and road damage. This section investigates particular types of road infrastructures including pavements, earthworks, bridges and tunnels and their anticipated degradation as a result of climate changes and hazards.

Figure 2.2. **Indicative climate trends, impacts and damages for roadways**

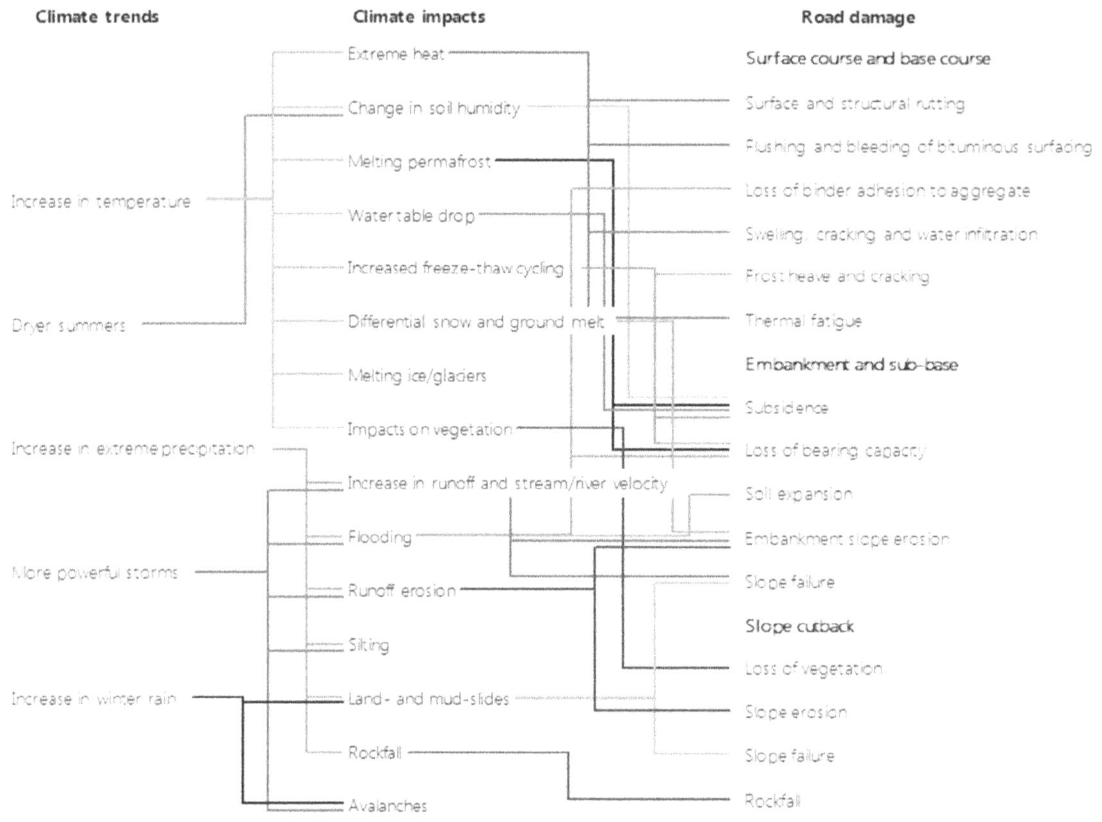

Source: Adapted from Parriaux, 2012.

Pavements

Pavements are most susceptible to extreme heat and moisture/precipitation levels. They are also exposed to damage and blockage from landslides and rock fall. Depending on the pavement type (flexible vs. rigid) weather impacts may differ. Flexible (asphalt) pavements are formed by a number of layers shown in Figure 2.3; the upper layer (surface course) is the asphalt layer, followed by the base and sub-base layers.

The service life of road structures (pavement and foundation) typically ranges from 40 to 50 years, depending upon its type (Meade and Janisch, 2003; Refsdal and Johansen, 2008) except for long-life concrete or polymerised pavements whose service life may be extended to 60 years (Hall et al., 2007). However, these lifetimes assume that the surface will be maintained and rehabilitated in intervals of 15-30 years (Li and Kaini, 2006; Refsdal and Johansen, 2008). Figure 2.4 presents a typical pavement life cycle under good maintenance practices and with periodic refurbishments and illustrates how this life cycle might change in areas where climate impacts lead to more rapid deterioration and earlier maintenance and refurbishment requirements. Not all regions, however, would be exposed to the same changes in life cycle and maintenance regimes. In the Province of Quebec, Bilodeau et al. (2013) find that pavement structures could see a 28% reduction in service life over current pavements with expected changes in climate. Modelling from Australia, on the other hand, indicates that under warmer and dryer conditions expected with climate change, pavement performance might in fact improve leading to fewer maintenance interventions and potentially longer life (Taylor and Philp, 2015).

Changes in temperature (higher average temperature, increase in the frequency of hot weather extremes and warm summer days, warmer winter temperatures and an increase in the number of freeze-thaw cycles) affect asphalt pavements in a number of ways as described below.[3]

Figure 2.3. **Typical (asphalt) road components: Pavement and foundation**

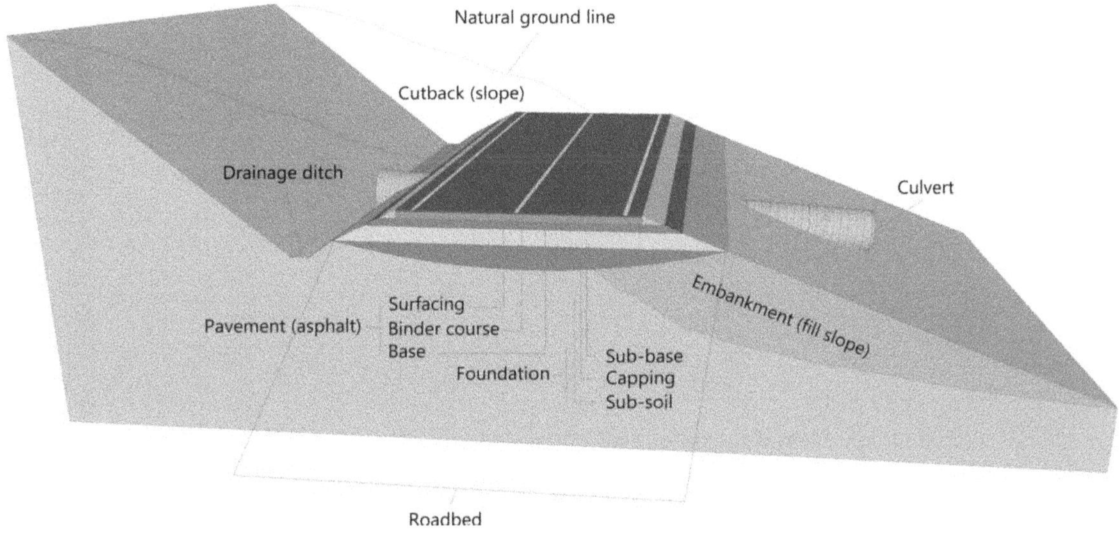

Higher temperatures: Flexible pavements

The increase in maximum pavement temperatures and the duration of hot spells increases the potential for asphalt deterioration via rutting and lateral displacement of asphalt under dynamic loading – especially on high traffic roads (see Figure 2.4). Higher ultraviolet radiation prematurely ages asphalt pavements and makes them brittle (less flexible) thus also contributing to asphalt surface cracking initiation and propagation which can initiate water damage to lower layers (Figure 2.5). These phenomena reduce comfort in the most benign cases or lead to loss of vehicle control and crashes in the worst cases. One potential remedy is to resurface with more rut-resistant mixtures or thin rut-resistant surfaces as temperatures increase. Alternatively, using higher temperature binder grades or binders that age more slowly when resurfacing could also reduce heat damage to pavements. However, in the case of increasing extreme temperatures, historical guidance on the specification of binder grades may no longer be adequate. Prolonged hot and dry conditions may also result in subgrade shrinkage and loss of uniform bearing capacity.

Another approach may be to increase the use of binder polymerisation. The latter strategy, though more expensive than current pavement materials, could increase the life of the wearing course beyond the typical ~20 year refurbishment cycle – and up to 40 years (ITF, 2008) . This may decrease the incidence of heat-related damage but could extend the life of some pavements into periods where more frequent winter precipitation or more extreme precipitation may become the norm. Both of these phenomena are potentially damaging to pavement as described below.

Figure 2.4. **Indicative changes in pavement life cycle and maintenance regimes under negative impacts from climate change**

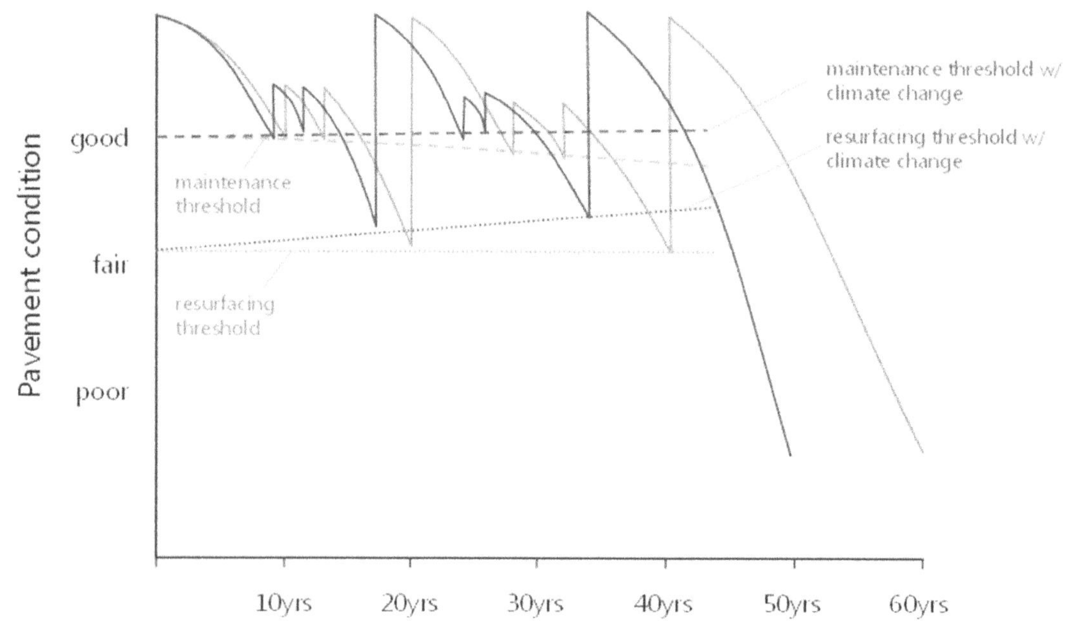

Figure 2.5. **Heat damage to asphalt pavements: Rutting and cracking**

Source: Left © W. Burda; Right © Oregon Department of Transportation.

Higher temperatures: Rigid pavement

Rigid (concrete) pavements consist of concrete slabs lain over the base, sub-base and sub-grade layers (replacing the asphalt surfacing, binder course and base illustrated in Figure 2.3). Traffic loads are taken on by the slabs and distributed more directly to the sub-base and sub-grade layers. Concrete and other rigid pavements are susceptible to heat warping, temperature-related curling and transverse crack formation (Willway et al., 2008). In general, concrete slabs are resistant to moisture effects but during extreme heat events, concrete pavements may experience "blow-ups" as moist base layers expand (see Figure 2.6).

Possible remedies include better accounting for the coefficient of thermal expansion and drying shrinkage for concrete, shorter joint spacing to reduce warp stress, using thicker slabs and/or less rigid base materials. Installing flexible expansion joints between slabs can also reduce the risk of blow-ups during extreme heat events. As with flexible pavements, drought conditions may give rise to damaging subgrade shrinkage and subsidence.

Figure 2.6. **Concrete slab pavement blow-up due to elevated heat and base humidity**

Source: © City of Champaign-Urbana.

An increase in average and extreme warm temperatures may have an impact on the scheduling of construction and maintenance activities as well. Dunne, Stouffer and John (2013) found that heat stress has already reduced labour capacity for outdoor work (all sectors, globally) during peak months by 10% from 2010 levels. This could increase to a 25% to 60% loss of labour capacity during the warmest months respectively for the RCP 4.5 and RCP 8.5 scenarios.[4] Some operations may have to be switched to night-time (possibly entailing higher costs) but warmer weather may also allow for more winter scheduling of work – unless winter moisture and precipitation levels render these operations impossible.

Warmer average winter temperatures and warmer winter extremes

Impacts of warmer average winter temperatures and warmer extreme cold temperatures are mixed depending on the context. Generally, warmer average winter temperatures and warmer winter extremes may *reduce* the depth of winter frost and possibly *reduce* the incidence of winter frost heave which can lead to pavement fatigue and local failure (e.g. potholes). This might entail a reduction in de-icing efforts, a relaxation of frost depth protection measures in some instances and a raising of low temperature asphalt binder grades. On the other hand, though evidence is mixed, warming winters could in some areas contribute to *increased* freeze-thaw cycling as temperatures rise to around the freeze point. This could lead to an *increase* in frost heave-induced damage to pavements. This would entail adjusting binder grades for flexible pavements and mitigating freeze-thaw cycling impacts on rigid pavements, especially as concerns the treatment of joints. More freeze-thaw cycling would also require more frequent de-icing applications in order to prevent loss of skid-resistance crashes. Because thaw-saturated soils lose bearing capacity, changes in the thaw cycling regime may also require more frequent or prolonged load restrictions for thawing roads entailing economic losses for commercial transport operators.

In northern latitudes, warmer winters (and summers) will lead to deeper permafrost melting resulting in damaging heaving movements that will impact the usability and safety of roads (see Figure 2.7). Many communities and industries in northern regions depend on winter access by ice roads and frozen rivers that have a greater load-bearing capacity than the oftentimes unpaved summer roads (if any). Warming trends have already reduced the yearly availability of seasonal ice-roads and this loss is likely to accelerate under warming trends (Stephenson, 2016). This results in increased access costs as alternative infrastructure will have to be upgraded or built, or loss of access and ensuing economic losses (Sawyer, 2014; Borkovic, Nolet and Roorda, 2015).

Figure 2.7. **Melting permafrost: Heave damage to roadway**

Source: Natural Resources Canada.

Increases in average and extreme precipitation, and flooding

Increased moisture levels have a damaging effect on pavement. Increased water presence strips aggregates from their binding material in the asphalt layer and contributes to its rapid deterioration. Higher average levels of precipitation reduce the structural carrying capacity of pavements due to higher moisture saturation levels. Ensuring positive cross-slopes can help with water evacuation thus reducing these impacts. Intense precipitation and storm surge can also lead to hydraulic-induced failures of embankments and foundations (see below) resulting in a total loss of pavements. Drainage and foundation-failures are the main source of climate risk for roads in regions experiencing higher average and extreme precipitation trends and coastal flooding.

More intense rainfall also has an impact on road safety. In order to improve visibility and reduce the incidence of crashes caused by loss of skid resistance (aquaplaning), many jurisdictions are investing in porous asphalt pavements (Stipanovic et al., 2015). These pavements, however, are generally susceptible to freeze-thaw damages outlined above unless properly drained.

Impacts from intermittent flooding can be mitigated by installing, upgrading and maintaining effective sub-drainage systems. Stream, river and coastal (wave and storm-surge) flooding can temporarily make roads unavailable. These phenomena can also cause kinetic impacts that result in partial or complete destruction of the pavement layer (see Figure 2.8). Prolonged submersion of roadways threatens the stability of embankments and foundations. These risks can be mitigated by increasing the use of bound materials in the base and foundation layers, elevating the roadway, or re-siting roads away from flood-prone areas. The latter two options are especially expensive.

Many countries have extensive networks of unpaved gravel roads, especially in rural areas. These roads typically carry light traffic but in many instances represent crucial links to isolated communities. These roads are especially vulnerable to increases in average and extreme precipitation levels (Aursand and Horvli, 2009). Changing climate regimes may require the upgrading of some of these in order to avoid excessive maintenance costs which will entail considerable upfront costs. In some cases, upgrading may be uneconomic entailing degraded access conditions and loss of viability for certain communities.

Figure 2.8. **Hurricane Sandy storm-surge damage on Highway 12 in North Carolina**

Source: © NCDOT Communications.

Relevance of climate change time-scales to adaptation of road pavements

Estimation of the service life of pavements and particularly their surface layer is directly related to the timing of potential climate change impacts. Since the life cycle of the pavement *surface* (surfacing and binder course) is relatively short (15-20 years), it seems likely that the normal scheduling of maintenance and resurfacing will allow for flexible adaptation to changing climate regimes. In many cases, decisions regarding which adaptation actions to deploy in response to changing temperature or precipitation trends can be made during the normal life cycle of road pavements. In some cases, accelerated deterioration, most likely linked to hydraulic damages, may require advancing certain maintenance and refurbishment actions.

Earthworks and geotechnical structures

Earthworks and geotechnical structures include the road/rail foundations (embankments) and corridor configuration (slopes and cuts) illustrated in Figures 2.3 and 2.16. These are typically soil- and sand-made, and are highly prone to inundation and hydraulic damage. Indeed, changes in precipitation intensity and frequency are more likely to affect structural integrity of roadway earthworks including road foundation (the substructure and sub-grade layers), and slopes than the pavement itself (Keller et al., 2011) (Parriaux, 2012).

Potential climate impacts on these structures are numerous. For example, erosion of road-side slopes can result from rainfall and water runoff along slopes (Xu et al., 2009). Slope stability (and the possibility of landslide and rockfall occurrence), is related to the groundwater level and degree of saturation[5] fluctuations in the slope (Dehn et al., 2000). Increased moisture reduces the cohesion and therefore the strength of soils (Samtani and Nowatzki, 2006). Along the same lines, intrusion of water in the road foundation through groundwater level rise or damage in the upper pavement layers (combined with increased rainfall), could also lead to erosion and saturation phenomena, which can again weaken road foundation. As with pavements, repeated or prolonged flooding of earthworks increases the risk of serious damage. Micro-flooding (e.g. localised impoundments) is often not expressly accounted for in earthwork design yet these relatively widespread and potentially damaging events are likely to increase in number with an increase in average and extreme precipitation (Polemio and Lollino, 2011). Weakened earthworks and foundations lose their bearing capacity and in extreme cases can lead to foundation washout or collapse (see Figure 2.9). In these instances, improving drainage and/or introducing hydraulic binding agents into foundation and earthwork materials may help.

In areas likely to experience hotter and dryer conditions and extended droughts, the structural integrity of earthworks may degrade due to desiccation (water removal) in soils containing fines (for example clay). In higher altitude mountainous areas and northern latitudes, increased permafrost melting and dynamic soil fluctuation can lead to loss of slope and cut cohesion resulting in rock-fall.

Figure 2.9. **Foundation washout and collapse**

Note: US Route 101 in Oregon and Oldbury rail Viaduct, UK
Source: Left, © Visitor7; Right, © David Stowell.

In addition to water-related climate change impacts, slopes and road foundations may be affected by changes in the frequency of freeze-thaw cycles. Increased freeze-thaw cycling reduces the effective stresses[6] or cohesive capacity of the materials forming earthworks. Another impact, also related to both weather and temperature, is the change in vegetation along slopes and embankments. While lack of vegetation (in cases of extreme dryness) could negatively impact slope stability (and lead to visibility-reducing and dangerous fires), rapid growth of plants may reduce the operability of a road (for example by limiting road visibility) and increase maintenance needs.

Extreme weather phenomena could be another source of earthwork degradation. Intense winds and severe storms for instance can cause rapid erosion of road-side slopes and unexpected landslides (Keller et al., 2011), while flooding and storm surge could lead to earthwork failure, particularly when drainage infrastructures and culverts are inadequately dimensioned.

All of the impacts outlined above hold true for earthworks and geotechnical components for all transport infrastructure, not just roadways. In addition, transport network planning for adaptation must account for the resistance of geotechnical components *outside* of the direct responsibility of many transport authorities. In particular climate change-related impacts on levees and seawalls that lead to breaches will have knock-on effects on transport systems and earthworks.

Relevance of climate change time-scales to adaptation of earthworks and geotechnical components

Because geotechnical elements and earthworks are typically longer-lived than pavements (or ballast, in the case of rail corridors), these infrastructure components will be exposed to changes in climate and thus more proactive planning may be required, especially in areas likely to experience increases in average and extreme precipitation and in coastal areas prone to storm damage and flooding.

Bridges

Bridges are probably the most complex and sensitive roadway infrastructure element. Because of their strategic role in spanning otherwise impassable landscape elements (streams, rivers, coastal waterways, canyons, etc.) their failure may result in large detour-related time losses. Sometimes, they may represent the sole link to communities, in which case their loss imposes extreme hardship on inhabitants.

Bridge design (and cost) is usually related to length, materials used, foundation capabilities and intended traffic capacity (Ryall et al., 2000). Because bridges represent relatively large-scale and strategic capital investments, their typical design life exceeds 60 years (details are presented in Table 2.5) and their actual useful life may extend many more years (or decades in some cases). For instance, nearly 30% of the road bridge stock in the United States was over 55 years old in 2013 (FHWA, 2013). This implies that, unlike other roadway elements such as pavement surfaces whose service life is approximately 20 years, bridges constructed today will almost certainly be exposed to future climate change. Furthermore, many of the bridges in use today were constructed using engineering standards that reference meteorological and climate conditions that are less and less representative of current (and likely future) conditions (Meyer et al., 2014; Nemry and Demirel, 2012). Bridge materials (concrete, steel, timber) have different properties with respect to temperature, water and other climate variable, and thus concrete and steel bridge components should be considered separately.

Table 2.5. **Service life for typical bridge components**

Component	Average service life
Deck	30-50 years
Superstructure	60-80+ years
Substructure	60-80+ years

Source: Compiled from Russel et al., 2004; Sohanghpurwala, 2006; Kaini and Li, 2006; Liang et al, 2009.

Bridges are made up of three major components: deck, superstructure (everything above and including the bearings) and substructure (all elements below the bearings). The deck is the roadway, railway or pedestrian-way surface of a bridge; decks are either concrete slabs or steel plates, stiffened in one or two directions (orthotropic decks) (Ryall et al., 2000), while their surface can be either asphalt or concrete. The superstructure includes the bridge spans, which support deck loads and connect substructure components. The superstructure can be made of concrete, steel or wooden beams, steel trusses, cables or other load bearing or load-distributing elements, depending on the bridge type and material used. In some cases, superstructures and decks are combined in a single component (for example in T-beam structures). Substructure components are those elements that support the superstructure and deck and distribute loads to the ground; these are abutments, piers and their foundation (see Figure 2.10). Most substructure elements (abutments, foundation) are concrete but piers could also be steel or composite (steel-concrete) – foundations usually include spread footings or piles.

Changes in average and extreme temperature will affect both the concrete and steel components of a bridge. Thermal expansion of steel elements or thermal mismatch between cement and aggregates of concrete elements can lead to deterioration which can weaken the structural strength of those elements (Ryall et al., 2000). Increased average and extreme temperatures can also result in a change of the thermal strain stress behaviour of structures which may lead to changes in performance. Tensile stresses in particular may display new and potentially damaging values and should be monitored. Adaptation efforts may include focusing on reducing heat absorption by structures by, for example, lighter, heat-reflective coatings (Santillán, Salete and Toledo, 2015).

Figure 2.10. **Typical bridge components**

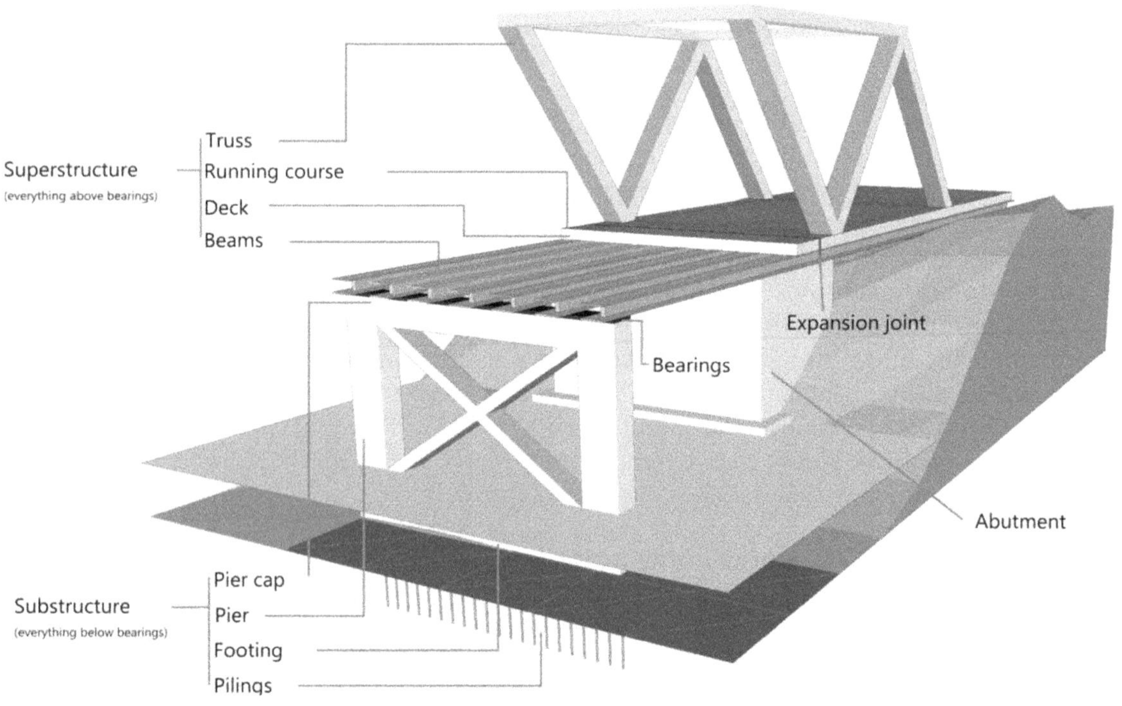

Changes in average and extreme temperature will affect both the concrete and steel components of a bridge. Thermal expansion of steel elements or thermal mismatch between cement and aggregates of concrete elements can lead to deterioration which can weaken the structural strength of those elements (Ryall et al., 2000).

Increased humidity and water infiltration, in conjunction with increased temperature, accelerates chemical deterioration of both steel and concrete components. Steel corrosion is a result of rusting due to moisture, while concrete corrosion can be chloride or carbonation induced (Figure 2.11). Increased atmospheric CO_2 concentrations accelerate carbonation damage to concrete and thus potentially expose steel reinforcing elements to corrosion. Carbonation-induced damage risks may rise significantly as CO_2 concentrations increase – (Stewart, Wang and Nguyen, 2012) find that these may increase by 16% by 2100. Concrete carbonation combined with expansive corrosion of steel reinforcement elements result in concrete cover cracking and spalling and a loss of structural capacity (Stewart, Wang and Nguyen, 2011). Since the increase in atmospheric CO_2 concentration is one of the most robust and predictable climate-relevant trends, there is a strong likelihood that transport authorities will see (and should plan for) more rapid carbonation-induced damages to concrete infrastructure. Increases in concrete thickness, improved concrete mixes and the application of coatings and barriers can help but will increase the cost of construction and maintenance (Stewart, Wang and Nguyen, 2012).

Chloride-induced corrosion is a significant threat to submerged or partially submerged concrete/steel infrastructure in coastal areas. It is not clear that climate change will modify the chlorination mechanisms though sea level rise and sea water infiltration of fresh water coastal bodies may see an increase in the exposure of concrete infrastructure to chloride-induced corrosion (Wang et al., 2011).

Figure 2.11. **Steel and concrete bridge component corrosion**

Source: Photos © Achim Hering.

Increased precipitation affects bridge components in multiple ways: the deck and superstructure may be damaged from water intrusion which will cause further corrosion and deterioration, particularly if the bridge's drainage system is not designed to absorb additional water volume. As for the substructure, rainfall, and storm flooding could alter water level and flow under the bridge, as well as soil properties in the vicinity of bridge foundation. In particular:

- Changes in water flow strength and level increases potentially damaging dynamic loading on submerged structures including abutments and piers (Radomski, 2002).
- Turbulent high velocity water flow around submerged bridge components can scour surrounding foundation and bank material leading to loss of structural support (Figure 2.12) (Radomski, 2002).
- Saturation in the vicinity of the bridge foundation may negatively affect the soil's effective stress and therefore its loading capacity; in such a case the soil fails by sinking or shifting and causes structure movement or damage.

Evidence from the United States indicates that 62% of over-water bridge failures are due to hydraulic causes (Cook, Barr and Halling, 2014). Wright et al. (2012) project that 10-20% of the current US over-water bridge stock could be at-risk for significant hydraulic damage by 2050, increasing up to 25% by 2100.

Figure 2.12. **Bridge pier scouring: Damage and displacement**

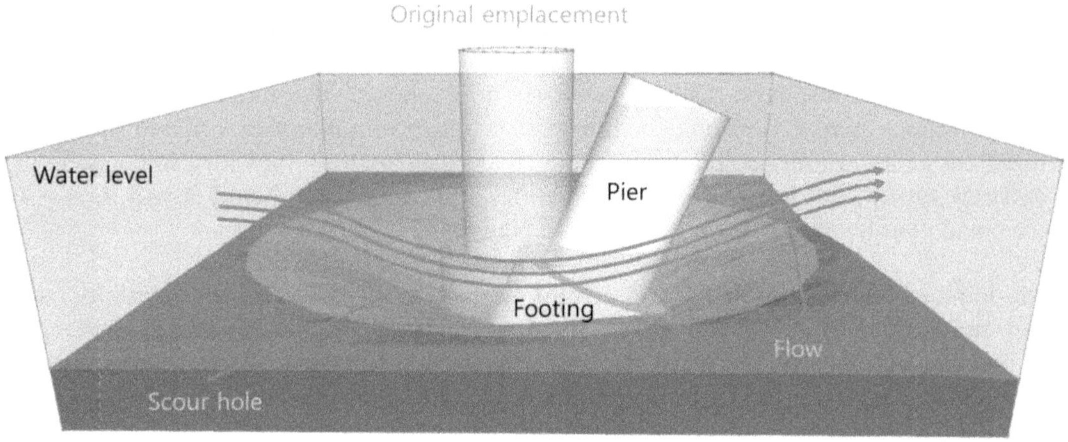

Hydraulic events such as scour and dynamic loading can lead to single-point failure or, in extreme cases, to multiple-point failures that compromise not only the integrity of the bridge itself but its approaches as well (Figure 2.13).

Figure 2.13. **Monsoon flooding-triggered bridge and road damages in Pakistan (2010)**

A. Scour-induced loss of embankment and abutment support.
B. Scour and dynamic loading loss of piers.
C. Scour-induced loss of embankment and foundation of approach road.
Source: Horace Murray.

Finally, extreme wind intensity may render bridges inaccessible for safety reasons and may cause damage when wind loads are exceeded. Climate change impacts on bridges are summarised in Table 2.6.

Table 2.6. **Climate change impacts on bridges**

Climate change variable	Impact to...	
	Concrete components	**Steel components**
Temperature changes	• Upper deck surface deterioration (as in pavements)	
	• Damage due temperature difference between cement and aggregate	• Damage due to thermal expansion of steel components
Increase in precipitation - moisture	• Chloride or carbonation induced corrosion • Substructure scouring • Foundation failing due to soil saturation	• Corrosion due to rusting.
Increase in atmospheric CO_2	• Carbonation induced corrosion	
Sea level rise	• Substructure scouring • Foundation failing due to soil saturation	• Corrosion due to rusting.
Extreme weather events	• Damage – collapse of structure	

Culverts and ditches

Culverts are arguably as critical, if not more critical, than bridges for ensuring high-quality transport services because they are both more common and more susceptible to damage and catastrophic failure and thus represent many more potential network failure points. Generally hidden and invisible to most transport system users, culverts play an essential role in maintaining the structural integrity of transport infrastructure. Placed wherever transport infrastructure cross drainage slopes, or where drainage is necessary from longitudinal drainage ditches, culverts pass water from one side of an infrastructure to the other (Figures 2.2 and 2.16). This prevents water from ponding on the upstream side (and thus weakening earthworks) or passing over and damaging road pavements, rail permanent ways or airport runways and taxiways. Ensuring adequate drainage also improves safety and improves user comfort. Ditches collect water from infrastructure and surrounding slopes and allow it to either percolate into the soil or be evacuated by subsurface drainage culverts. In urban areas, open ditch-culvert systems are replaced by extensive closed underground storm water drainage systems.

Culverts are relatively long-lived infrastructure made either of corrugated sheet metal piping (less expensive), high density polyethylene or polyvinyl chloride pipes, or of concrete (concrete box culverts – more expensive). The service life of culverts should at least match the service life of the infrastructure in which it is embedded since culvert replacement can completely disrupt traffic and lead to traveller time losses (Schall et al., 2012). Perrin and Jhaveri (2004) report that US transport agencies assumed lifetimes of 50-100 years for concrete culverts, 30-100 years for plastic culverts and 30-50 years for corrugated metal pipe culverts. As such, existing culverts will be increasingly exposed to climate conditions for which they were not designed and new culvert design specifications will have to account for climate change over their lifespan.

Figure 2.14. **Road damage from culvert failure and washout**

Source: Left, © Seattle Municipal Archives; Right, © Daniel Case.

Once installed, culverts generally prompt little attention and making the case for continued and proactive maintenance has not necessarily proven easy in many jurisdictions, especially in light of budgetary constraints (Perrin and Jhaveri, 2004; Kalantari, 2011). Culvert failure, on the other hand, typically elicits significant attention as it implies road and track closures and significant repair and re-routing costs (see Figure 2.14).

Culverts can fail in multiple ways. Both steel and concrete culverts are susceptible to corrosion (rust for steel and carbonation for concrete). This corrosion weakens the structural strength of these materials (leading to collapse in some cases) or allows water to seep into the surrounding structural soil and initiating erosive damage. In fact many culvert failures can be traced to failure of the soil-pipe structure (Tenbusch, Dorwart and Tenbusch, 2009; Schall et al., 2012). This failure is typically initiated in three ways (Tenbusch, Dorwart and Tenbusch 2009; 2013):

- when water enters into areas from which it was originally excluded (in the case of seepage or piping)
- when extreme flows lead to scouring and erosion of embankments and structural soils in the inlet area (including behind protective wings) and at the outlet
- because of debris blockage, pipe collapse or hydrostatic pressure.

Increased average precipitation and extreme precipitation levels will have an impact on culvert performance and these changes should be incorporated into culvert design. Culverts are designed to handle peak flows that are likely to be encountered in their location. The determination of these peak discharge rates is based on methods[7] that either directly or indirectly incorporate factors such as historic climate variables (24-hour precipitation, intensity-density-frequency curves and precipitation distribution input values), slopes and size of the catchment area. Correction factors accounting for lakes and other impoundments, the degree of vegetative cover or soil permeability or for climate change can be applied to these calculations (Kalantari, 2011; Meyer et al., 2014).

As it would be uneconomic to build culverts to handle all possible extreme precipitation scenarios, a decision is typically made on the return period to plan for in terms of the amount of flow to be handled in a given period of time. If climate change leads to more intense precipitation extremes, existing culvert design may prove inadequate leading to ponding on the upstream side and prolonged high-velocity flows. Both of these may initiate the type of failure points outlined above.

Climate change may have an impact on other variables besides precipitation in the peak flow calculations for culverts. Soils typically absorb a significant amount of precipitation with the remaining fraction working its way into the waterway network. Climate-related changes to soil permeability and absorption rates will change the precipitation-runoff factors that are typically built into culvert size calculations. For example, since highly desiccated (and compacted) soils lose their absorptive capacity, extreme precipitation events (which are predicted to increase in places even where average levels of precipitation will decrease) will result in higher rates of runoff to be handled by culvert structures (Meyer et al., 2014). A similar loss of soil permeability occurs in the case of winter rains on frozen (or near-frozen) soils which would lead to elevated runoff and culvert flow duration (Kalantari, 2011).

Several options exist to address potential culvert damage from extreme precipitation. These include re-sizing the dimension of the culvert, protecting embankments from scour by adding headwalls, side wings or endwalls or by preventing excessive scour damage at the outlet. These decisions are typically taken on the basis of first-order hydraulic considerations. However, many soil-pipe failures are in part the result of debris accumulation and the ensuing loss of culvert capacity. It may very well be that a properly dimensioned culvert may still fail if wood debris and sediment have reduced its effective diameter leading to ponding, deformation and scour dynamics that were unforeseen. Culvert performance is perhaps more a result of adequate maintenance regimes than adequate design. This is one area where authorities often lack budget as well as adequate knowledge pertaining to the condition of their culvert stock.

Tunnels

Tunnels and other underground structures are often designed to last for 100 years and are scarcely affected by weather conditions (Schiessl et al., 2004). However, certain weather-related hazards and particularly flooding may render the tunnel temporarily unavailable or damage the structure and the tunnel's equipment (Bobylev, 2009). In some cases, a rise in underground water level (due to extreme rainfall or storm surge – see Figure 2.15), could affect a tunnel's structural integrity (Bobylev, 2009). Tunnel and underground flooding will also have an impact on networks and infrastructure (power, telecoms, signaling in the case or public transport and rail) which can render essential services inoperable for extended periods of time. Also, temperature changes may impact the operation and performance of a tunnel's ventilation system (Bobylev, 2009).

Figure 2.15. **Flooded NYC tunnel due to Hurricane Sandy storm surge and infiltration**

Source: Left and right, © New York City Metropolitan Transit Authority.

Railway infrastructure

Railway networks are of mixed vintage across many countries with many components (bridges, tunnels, embankments and cuts) dating back to the 19th century. These components were designed for trains not capable of operating over more than very shallow gradients. Consequently, rail alignments of that vintage (and up through the 20th century) required extensive use of slope cuts and embankments to level the track profile. Though generally stable, these earthworks of uncertain quality and of sometimes rudimentary design (compared to modern standards) are susceptible to failure, especially under a changing climate and hydrologic regimes. Rail earthworks are similar in nature to those supporting roads and they share many of the same vulnerabilities. They are vulnerable to changes in precipitation and humidity patterns, flooding and water ingress. In coastal areas, they are vulnerable to wave action, storm surges and flooding (DfT, 2014) (see Figure 2.16). Finally, as with road maintenance, increased summer temperatures may limit the time available for track maintenance and this may not be compensated by milder (but wetter) winter temperatures in the Northern Hemisphere. Due to the need for relatively warm ambient temperatures necessary for stress-free setting of rails, the potential loss of summer maintenance opportunities may have knock-on effects on system performance as discussed further.

Damage to rail earthworks and geotechnical components reduce the bearing capacity of the ballast and tracks which may require reduced train operating speeds. Compromised earthworks pose a risk to the integrity of the track system and in some cases may result in a complete failure of the track foundation resulting in steep repair costs and time losses for passengers. More recent components, including those that make up high-speed rail networks, are built to more exacting standards and in some cases expressly account for potential climate change in their design but remain vulnerable to changes in precipitation patterns and intensities as well as to flooding. Despite commonalities with road infrastructure, rail systems do present unique vulnerabilities relating to the track structure, overhead components and signalling elements; these are addressed in the next section.

Figure 2.16. **Impacts of storm-related embankment scour**

Note: Wave damaged to rail infrastructure on Tillamook Bay Railroad (left) and Dawlish railroad line washout (right).
Source: Left, © Chris Updegrave; Right, © Lewis Clarke.

Railway tracks

The railway track structure consists of rails, sleepers and joints; they form a grid which is itself embanked in the ballast layer consisting of gravel or rocks (Figure 2.17), or is placed over concrete slabs (usually in stations and metro systems). The service life of rail track components for railways in the USA is presented in Table 2.7. Because of their relatively long service life, rail track structure components will almost certainly be impacted by mid- to long-term changes in climate variables. This, coupled with the long-lived nature of rail geotechnical elements and earthworks, makes rail systems especially vulnerable to climate impacts.

The rails themselves are particularly vulnerable to hot temperature extremes and wide temperature amplitudes. This is especially the case for continuously welded[8] rail which is the standard for modern railways. Thermal expansion of welded rails due to temperatures that are significantly above the rail's installation temperature or "anchoring" temperature (rail's neutral temperature) causes compressive stresses which in turn lead to the phenomenon of buckling (Lindgren et al., 2009; Nguyen et al., 2012), shown in Figure 2.18. The vulnerability of rails to track buckling is a function of thermal-induced compressive stress, weakened track and ballast conditions and the dynamic loading of tracks by trains. In a warming climate, it makes sense to select a progressively higher rail neutral temperature during installation and to be particularly vigilant to rail longitudinal, lateral and vertical movement. High temperatures and wide temperature amplitudes (over a short period of time) may also require monitoring and possibly adjusting train loads which may have an impact on network capacity (Nemry and Demirel, 2012).

Figure 2.17. **Typical railway track (with ballast)**

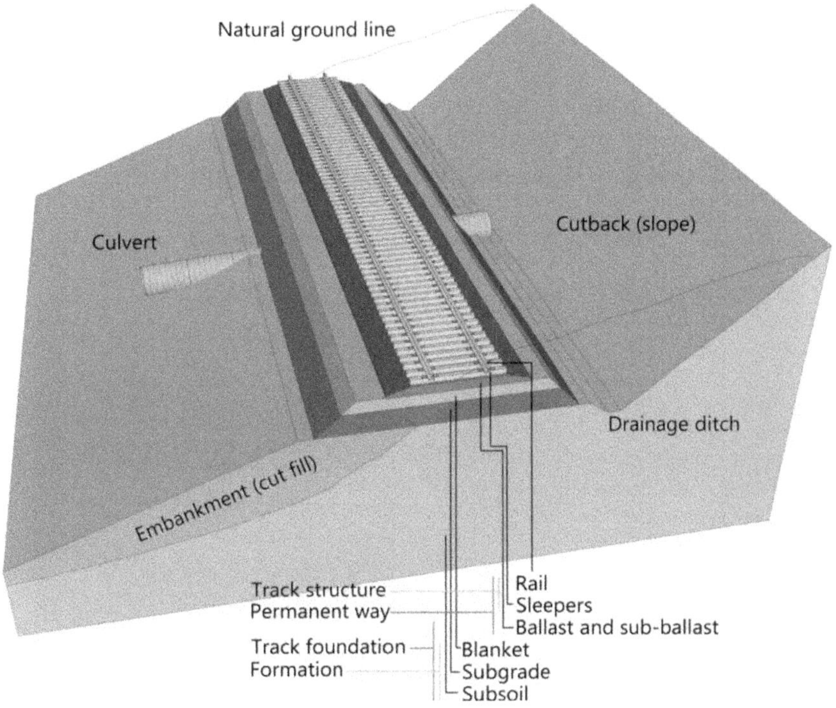

Table 2.7. **Railway component service life**

Component	Maximum service life range
Timber sleepers	35 years
Concrete sleepers	55 years
Continuously welded rails (CWR)	70 years
Bolt joint tails	60 years
Ballast	>60 years

Source: ARUP, 2008.

Railway infrastructure and extreme weather events

As in the case of roadway infrastructure, railway infrastructure such as tracks, earthworks, bridges and tunnels are highly prone to extreme weather phenomena. Flooding in particular, has a long history of causing significant loss of temporary availability and damages to railway infrastructures worldwide. Compared to roadway pavements and foundations, the lateral resistance of track structure permanent ways and their vulnerability to erosion and subsidence is low when exposed to extreme precipitation and associated hydraulic forces.

A change in winter precipitation regimes may give rise to increased wet precipitation in near-freezing conditions. The icing that results in these circumstances can damage overhead catenaries and other rail superstructure leading to delays and loss of service (Figure 2.19).

Figure 2.18. **Heat-induced track buckling**

Source: © ABproTWE.

Figure 2.19. **Ice damage to rail overhead structures and storm-fall on rail tracks**

Source: Left, © Danilo Rozman; Right, © Metropolitan Transportation Authority of the State of New York.

Increases in the incidence of strong storms and extreme wind, combined or not with a CO_2-induced increase in trackside vegetation, would contribute to network disruptions due to more frequent tree fall and other debris (Figure 2.19) unless track-side vegetation is more proactively managed. Finally, as with road infrastructure, an increase in the incidence of drought will impact trackside vegetation and can lead to erosion due to loss of vegetation or more frequent fires that may reduce visibility and damage rail-related structures. These potential impacts should be accounted for in trackside vegetation management programmes.

Urban public transport networks

Public transport services are delivered across multiple modes and infrastructure and as such, they are vulnerable to many of the hazards identified in previous sections. Public transport networks also serve to evacuate populations exposed to extreme weather events and their localised or systemic failures may have knock-on social impacts, especially concerning urban populations that are dependent on public transport services. Beyond the "generic" climate impacts to drainage systems, roads, rails, bridges, tunnels and geotechnical works outlined in this chapter, several public-transport-specific hazards also exist. These relate to flooding of underground subway systems and to public transport operations.

Figure 2.20. **Raised subway entrance to prevent pluvial tunnel flooding, Sun Yat-Sen Memorial Station, Taipei Metro, Taipei**

Source: © mailer_diablo, Wikimedia Commons.

Increased flooding risk, whether pluvial or linked to storm surges and sea level rise, pose particular threats to underground subway systems. These systems are susceptible to flooding which not only temporarily interrupts services, but also entails significant material losses to tunnels, signalling systems and subway stations. Saltwater encroachment can be particularly damaging due to its corrosive effects on electrical systems. Pluvial risk can be mitigated by designing passive rainwater evacuation and management systems, in order to avoid an accumulation of water in the subway, and by installing and maintaining emergency pumping capacity to evacuate water from the subway system. Many subways exposed to frequent or powerful rainfall have raised subway entrances in order to prevent surface runoff flooding (see Figure 2.20). Subway systems are also frequently vulnerable to coastal or fluvial flooding. In those instances, storm gates, temporary storm dams or inflatable tunnel plugs can reduce or prevent floodwaters from propagating through tunnel systems (Figure 2.21).

Public transport services are also susceptible to a number of indirect climate and weather impacts. That can impact operations. As noted above, public transport can serve to help evacuate areas impacted by extreme weather events. They also serve a crucial function in maintaining accessibility in cities during and after extreme weather events. The experience with Hurricane Sandy in New York City highlighted many operational impacts that could be expected to increase as the frequency of extreme weather events increases. These impacts include the need for redundant or excess capacity (provided in part in New York City by bicycles and for-hire van services); the ability to deploy temporary measures to replace the loss of subway services (The Metropolitan Transit Authority, the Department of Transport and the New York Police Department created a pop-up bus rapid transit system overnight to ensure service continuity despite the flooding of several subway tunnels); and the need to adapt operations to the overall loss of accessibility – particularly in light of staff access (many MTA workers were housed in temporary accommodations near depots in order to ensure that they could work their shifts); and degraded command-and-control facilities (Kaufman et al., 2012).

Figure 2.21. **Post Hurricane Sandy trials of inflatable bladder to seal off subway tunnels from flooding**

Source: New York City Metro Transit Authority.

Ports

Global sea level rise poses a threat to all low-lying coastal infrastructures, including roads, rail corridors and airports. Ports, however, by their nature, are especially exposed to sea level rise, estuarine flooding and storms including the damaging effects of storm surges that may exacerbate the impacts of rising sea levels. Port activity is also dependent on good access to the hinterland and thus ports are vulnerable to the potentially damaging impacts of climate change on connecting infrastructure. As with other trade-dependent infrastructure, a changing climate may lead to shifts in global trade patterns (and in particular to trade in agricultural products) which would impact demand for port services. Crucially, many major ports play a critical role in global supply chains – any significant loss or degradation of service would have significant knock-on effects on global supply chain performance.

Port systems are comprised of numerous components and are dependent on multiple service providers and actors. Each of these may be differently exposed to climate hazards implying a need for an overarching framework to better capture port climate vulnerabilities. Stenek et al. (2011), (Becker, et al, 2013) and Scott et al. (2013) propose such a framework to gauge the vulnerability of port system sub-components to climate change. In particular, Stenek et al. (2011) identifies specific vulnerabilities related to navigation, berthing, material handling, vehicle movement, goods storage and transportation. The material impacts of potential changes in climate regimes on each of these sub-systems are, for the most part, not qualitatively different than for the other transport modes already described. Asphalt surfaces are prone to heat damage; port superstructures are exposed to wind damage; wave action and flooding can lead to erosion of embankments and abutments; electrical and other support systems may be prone to damage due to flooding, winds and heat; operations may have to be suspended during heat extremes and concrete materials may be exposed to accelerated rates of carbonation- or chloride-induced corrosion. As with other transport systems, co-sited infrastructure and/or simultaneous or successive climate-related stressors may lead to broad and multi-point failures that may be difficult to predict if each component is analysed in isolation. Port systems do, however, face certain unique hazards related to changes in wave regimes and heights and the impacts of sea level rise and storm surges on breakwaters, quays and protective coastal infrastructure adjacent to port facilities (Becker et al., 2013).

Inland waterways

Inland waterway infrastructure, including groynes, training walls, rip-rap, quays, and locks, are exposed to many of the same climate stressors as other transport networks – and in particular to flood-related impacts. The waterway itself may also be subject to temporary incapacity due to winter icing. In addition, inland navigation is highly sensitive to prevailing water levels with low levels imposing lower load factors for vessels and increased costs per tonne transported for operators (Jonkeren, Jourquin and Rietveld, 2011). Projected changes in climate may have an impact on all of these elements with sometimes positive and sometimes negative outcomes for inland navigation.

Inland navigation is dependent on three elements; the river or canal itself including its geometry and hydromorphology, waterway infrastructure that either stabilises the navigable part of the channel or renders the canal operational and the level of water discharge in the waterway (Simoner et al., 2012). Episodes of intense rainfall may lead to elevated water velocities and erosion of river banks, bridge abutments and other infrastructure elements. Changes in river flow characteristics may also impact rates and location of sedimentation which will, in turn, imply changed fairway maintenance practices and may increase dredging requirements. In addition, flooding may lead to short-term river closures due to safety concerns. These types of incidents are projected to increase in the Northern Hemisphere leading to more elevated maintenance costs and time losses for operators and shippers. On the other hand, loss of waterway capacity due to winter icing and ice flows are projected to become much less frequent (Leviakangas, et al., 2012). Given that the latter implies much longer periods of suspension of navigation than the former, this might suggest that overall waterway availability in light of flooding and icing may improve in the Northern Hemisphere though this finding is highly dependent of the local context of different waterway basins (Jonkeren et al., 2013; Leviakangas et al., 2012; Simoner et al., 2012; KLIWAS, 2015).

Inland waterways are highly dependent on rates of water discharge and resultant water levels. Flooding, as described above, can lead to temporary suspension of navigation but low water levels resulting from drought can lead to prolonged loss of capacity of the waterway system or to closures in extreme cases. Rivers and canals can be both rain-fed and meltwater fed. Increases in winter precipitation in the form of rain are expected to lead to higher seasonal discharge rates and in their extreme, these might hamper navigation and damage infrastructure. At the same time, a shift from frozen to wet precipitation will lead to a decrease in the melt-water component of navigable waterways. This implies that springtime and summer water levels may drop as a shrinking ice pack upstream will lead to lower discharge rates. In addition, higher temperatures and decreases in summertime precipitation may further exacerbate low water levels. Projections for both the US and Northern Europe indicate little loss of wintertime capacity but a sometimes significant drop of summertime capacity (and a concomitant increase in operator and shipper costs) due to low water levels (Jonkeren et al., 2013; KLIWAS, 2015). This negative trend becomes especially apparent in the second half of the 21st century (KLIWAS, 2015; Simoner et al., 2012).

Adaptation responses may include low-drought ship designs and other vessel-level technology changes and increased investment in water retention facilities. The former could be deployed over time as conditions warrant and as the vessel fleet naturally turns. Because inland waterway vessels typically have a life of approximately 50 years, planning for fleet adaptation should start now. Longer-term investments in water retention capacity or river infrastructure would entail significant higher investment levels that would have to be evaluated despite a high degree of uncertainty regarding the direction and ultimate scale of changes in water level (ECCONET, 2012). At the same time, uncertainty remains regarding future adaptation costs for competing networks like rail and road that could carry at least some of the goods transported by inland waterway (Jonkeren, Jourquin and Rietveld, 2011) .

Figure 2.22. **Storm surge and flooding vulnerability for coastal airports**

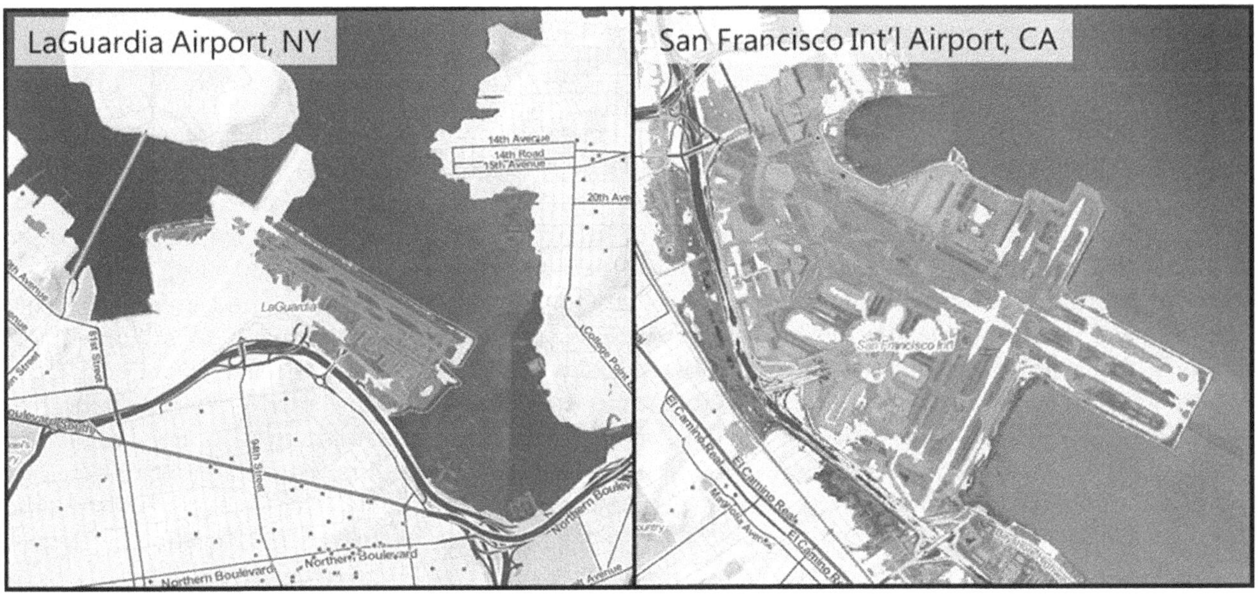

Note : Potential inundation for 91 cm (3ft.) surge/sea level rise (blue shading) over average local high tide level (not accounting for local flood defence infrastructure)
Source: Climate Central.

Airports and air transport

As with ports, airports are facilities which include multiple infrastructure components: roadway-type infrastructures (runways, taxiways, access roads, etc.), buildings (terminals, repair warehouses, control towers) and outdoor navigation aids, control and communication equipment. These sub-components are exposed to similar hazards and vulnerabilities as for other transport networks. In addition, airports and air services display some unique vulnerabilities as outlined in (Eurocontrol, 2013). More extreme precipitation and winds can lead to reduced airport capacity and outright interruptions of flight services in some cases. Insofar as extreme precipitation and storm events are expected to become more frequent, these will have knock-on impacts on air travel and delays. Localised changes in wind patterns and convective weather may also impact flight operations and lead to a loss of capacity and delays. Baglin (2012) summarises possible climate change impacts to airport infrastructures as follows:

- Temperature and precipitation changes will have the same impacts to airport pavements and earthworks as in roadway infrastructures. Further, increased salt and chemical usage for de-icing as a result of more frequent low temperatures will have a further negative impact on airport pavements.

- Sea level rise could result in inundation of coastal airports (Figure 2.22).
- Extreme weather phenomena such as storm surges and strong winds may damage outdoor airport equipment and buildings.

Costs of extreme weather: Big (and uncertain) numbers

The previous sections outline the multiple hazards that are linked to extreme weather and to climate change. The direct impacts on infrastructure are but one part of the overall costs that extreme weather imposes on society: users and operators suffer losses of income and material damages to vehicles and cargo and society pays for extreme weather-related crashes in the form of medical care costs and reduced labour inputs.

The direct economic costs associated with the impact of climate change and extreme weather on land-based transportation systems relate to the monetary cost of repairing or rebuilding damaged infrastructure. Analysis of direct disaster costs on a global scale has shown that the annual direct losses from significant natural catastrophes increased by at least an order of magnitude from the 1950s to the 1990s, with these costs inflated by another factor of two when damage from lesser weather events are included (Auld et al., 2006). In the Australian context, a review of natural catastrophes between 1980 and 2008 showed that for the decade 1999 to 2008 insured losses were approximately USD 7 billion, almost doubling the losses recorded for the previous two decades (MunichRe, 2009). Climate change has been identified as a contributing factor to increasing event costs, along with population growth, urbanisation of vulnerable regions, the concentration of population and assets, improved living standards, vulnerability of modern technology systems and societies reliance on uninterrupted service, increased insurance, and global networking (e.g. tourism) (Auld et al, 2006; MunichRe, 2010). The greatest public costs have been found to be related to disaster assistance, and road maintenance, relocation and repair (Middlemann, 2007).

Aside from the direct costs related to infrastructure damages, substantial indirect costs are likely to be experienced because of network effects including costs due to delays, losses from toll roads, freight supply interruption, detours and trip cancellations (Middlemann, 2007; Garnaut, 2008; Koetse and Rietveld, 2009).

Schweikert et al. (2014) estimates climate change adaptation costs for roads and the counterfactual in 10 countries based on the use of a software decision support tool – the Infrastructure Support Planning System (ISPS). This tool investigates infrastructure-linked adaptation costs across a number of areas, including planning, environment, service continuity and social impacts. ISPS evaluates the costs of climate change on two levels. The first based on a proactive "adapt" approach which seeks to make road systems more resilient to climate change by adapting changes in design and construction standards. The second approach, a more reactive "no-adapt" strategy looks solely at the damage and maintenance costs implied by no change in design standards. The approach embedded in the ISPS adopts several performance metrics namely incurred fiscal expenditures, opportunity costs for those expenditures and a "regret" metric. The latter evaluates the amount of money that could be lost if the adopted strategy (adapt vs. no-adapt) is not warranted. It is the potential cost of "over-protection" in the case of the "adapt" strategy and the cost of "under-protection" in the case of the "no-adapt" strategy.

Table 2.8. **Summary of yearly adaptation costs and associated metrics for 10 selected countries in the 2050s**

	Avg. Annual cost Adapt **USD million**		**Avg. Annual cost** No-adapt **USD million**		**Opportunity cost** Adapt		**Opportunity cost** No-adapt		Adapt **"regret" USD million**		No-adapt **"regret" USD million**	
	Median	Max.	Median	Max.	Median	Max.	Median	Max.	Median	Max.	Median	Max.
Bolivia	6.6	8.4	16.1	56.4	38%	96%	45%	165%	115.7	449.0	298.4	1083.5
Cameroun	3.0	5.7	5.6	15.7	21%	31%	23%	51%	50.6	116.2	168.8	378.8
Croatia	2.3	12.2	2.2	27.3	2%	12%	1%	12%	12.7	78.2	48.1	450.2
Ethiopia	5.0	6.6	16.3	50.9	27%	40%	39%	117%	85.9	227.7	409.2	1220.3
Italy	106.1	153.4	175.4	534.2	8%	11%	9%	16%	1016.6	1524.6	5100.0	9648.1
Japan	122.5	435.6	276.4	1062.6	4%	12%	5%	15%	1168.4	3530.9	6418.5	21020.4
New Zealand	5.8	10.1	8.9	17.2	3%	4%	3%	4%	105.2	193.1	268.9	400.9
Philippines	29.1	32.1	33.9	128.5	44%	48%	56%	88%	340.0	390.8	1715.9	2718.1
Sweden	31.3	103.8	34.5	121.1	6%	13%	6%	14%	1170.6	2603.6	1299.7	2897.0
Venezuela	17.0	20.3	59.4	78.2	16%	19%	25%	33%	192.6	255.9	1219.6	1633.8

Source: Schweikert et al., 2014.

The results outlined in Table 2.8 highlight that proactive adaptation approaches always deliver greater benefits than reactive no-adapt strategies, albeit the benefits (and regrets) vary across regions and levels of economic development. For low income countries (that also display low shares of paved, all-season roads) annual average costs in the 2050s are relatively low (given the lower value of the existing and new road stock) but these represent very high opportunity costs. These findings indicate that for the median ISPS results Bolivia could nearly double its road stock, and Cameroun, Ethiopia and the Philippines could considerably expand their road stock by the 2050s, even with proactive adaptation strategies and minimal or no climate impacts. Higher income countries display higher average annual costs by the 2050s in both the proactive and reactive cases due to extensive all-season paved road networks (and higher construction and maintenance costs). Opportunity costs for these countries are markedly lower in both proactive and reactive cases and the difference between each case is generally lower than for developing countries.

In terms of adaptation or no-adaptation "regret" – that is the amount a country might overspend if taking a proactive approach in the absence of climate change or, conversely, the monetised damage that might occur if a country takes no action other than maintenance and climate change impacts do manifest themselves – the findings in Schweikert et al. (2014) are clear. For both the median and maximum impact range and across all countries studied, a reactive no-adapt approach entails greater regret and costs than a proactive adapt approach. The spread between regret and no-regret outcomes differs greatly across countries however. In Sweden the range is quite narrow – USD 2.6 billion vs. USD 2.9 billion in the median case, whereas in Cameroun those figures are USD 50.6 and USD 168.8, respectively. These findings suggest that while all countries benefit from pro-active adaptation strategies, some countries clearly benefit more.

Nokkala et al. (2012) estimates that the European Union's 27 member states face EUR 15 billion in extreme weather-related costs. This cautious estimate is about 0.1% of the EU-27 GDP, and about EUR 30 annual extra cost to each EU-27 citizen in 2010. These figures were estimated by the Extreme

Weather impacts on European Networks of Transport (EWENT) project and they represented minimum conservative estimates. Whether these costs are significantly on the rise can only be speculated, but the general consensus among researchers is that societies should be prepared for an increase on the basis of this report's current understanding of climate science.

Figure 2.23. **Upward trends in extreme weather occurrences with loss-resulting consequences**

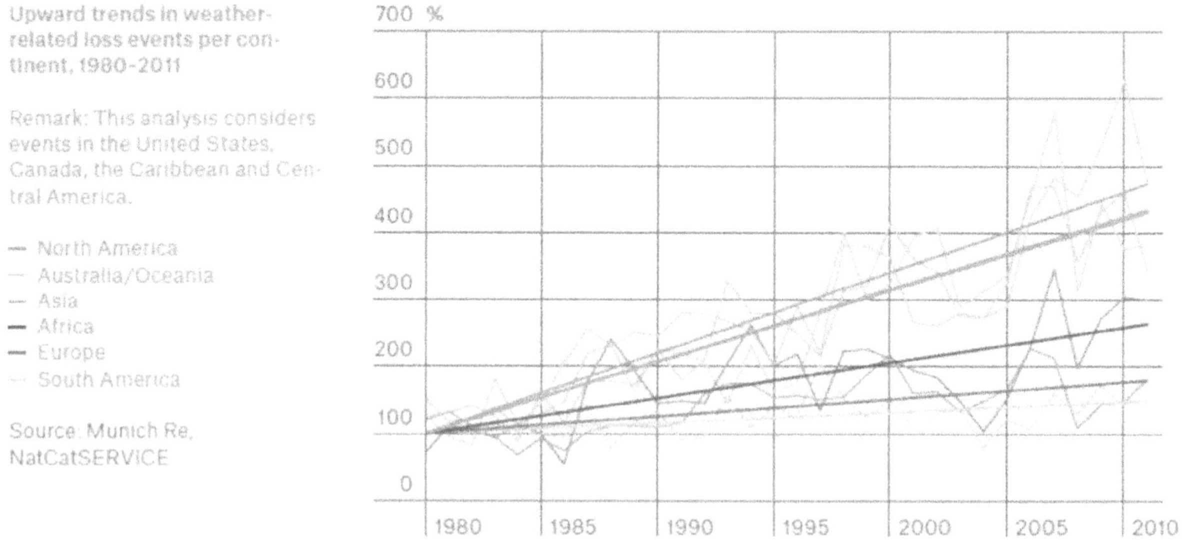

Source: MunichRe, 2012.

Furthermore, only recently have extreme weather costs drawn the attention of project financiers, insurers and their clients. The awareness of these costs has generated both business prospects and managerial challenges. For example, large first and re-insurers have identified new potential private and institutional customers, who want to hedge against extreme weather hazards. MunichRe (2012) has identified clear increasing trends in all types of meteorological and climatological events as well as in the losses these have entailed (Figure 2.23).

While the costs and consequences of extreme weather have been studied on an aggregate level, the tools for internalising the adverse effects and risks are by and large still missing. This internalisation is crucial especially in decisions on new transport system investments. However, climate risk is not the only issue assessed in investment appraisal. Some countries already widely internalise different external effects and risks, such as environmental impacts (noise, emissions and other items) (Maibach et al., 2008), but still in many countries even basic appraisal methods are lacking in investment decisions. Therefore the inclusion of extreme weather risks may be a novel element in many investment appraisal processes.

The costs and benefits of climate change have often been assessed on an aggregate level with varying estimates of both input parameters and selected future scenarios. This leads to a vision of the world where future benefits and costs as well as states-of-the-world can differ significantly from each other. Generally, the analysis and guidance received by policy makers is dominated by macro-level and general analysis of climate change impacts, as has been the case for the Stern Review (HM Treasury, 2012; for others, e.g. de Bruin et al., 2009; World Bank, 2012; HM Government, 2011)

Two recent EU projects assessed the impacts of climate change and extreme weather conditions on transport systems: EWENT and WEATHER. The WEATHER project aimed at identifying risks, economic impacts, and suitable crises management and transport adaptation strategies for all modes of transport across Europe. The EWENT project looked more deeply into long-term weather scenarios and the sensitivities of transport modes by following a standard risk assessment process.[9]

The WEATHER project considered the following extreme events: hot and cold spells, floods, landslides, wild fires and storms. Data were gathered through studies of various weather phenomena on transport in North America, Australia, Europe and New Zealand, a review of damage reports from six countries and an assessment of available transport operator data for some European transport networks. For the assessment period 1998 to 2010, the total costs borne by the transport sector (damages, repair and maintenance costs of infrastructures, vehicle damages, increased system operation costs, etc.) across all weather phenomena were estimated at EUR 2.5 billion per year. The indirect costs of transport disruptions on other sectors were estimated at EUR 1 billion per year. Projections for 2040–2050 (based on predictions of extremes taken from the EWENT project) suggest that rail will face the highest cost increase, with particular emphasis on the British Islands, central Europe and Scandinavia, mostly due to increases in hydrological extremes (Sanchez et al., 2012).

The EWENT project assessed average annual costs due to weather extremes for the current (1998–2010) and a future (2041–2070) time period. Costs comprised accident costs, time costs, infrastructure damage and maintenance, and effects on freight and logistics. EWENT estimated costs from extreme weather events in the baseline period of more than EUR 15 billion, which was dominated by the costs of road accidents (Table 2.9). This estimate was more than four times above the estimates of direct and indirect costs from the WEATHER project (Table 2.10). The main reasons for this difference were a wider definition of extreme events in EWENT, inclusion of externalities (accidents), and the explicit consideration of non-motorised travel and logistics among other aspects, which were omitted by the WEATHER project.

Table 2.9. **EWENT project's estimates on current extreme weather costs for the EU-27 transport system**

Mode	Present costs due to extreme weather, including all phenomena (ca. 2010)				
	Accidents	Time costs	Infrastructure		Freight & logistics
			Physical infra	Maintenance	
Road	**>10 bill. €/a,** mostly borne by the society	**0.5–1.0 bill. €/a,** mostly borne by road commuters	**ca. 1 bill. €/a,** mostly borne by infrastructure managers, ultimately by the taxpayers	**ca. 0.2 bill. €/a,** mostly borne by public infrastructure managers and hence ultimately by the taxpayers	**1–6 bill. €/a,** mostly borne by the shippers
Rail	**>0.1 bill. €/a,** mostly borne by the society	**>10 mill. €/a,** borne by the commuters	**>0.1 bill. €/a,** mostly borne by rail infrastructure managers (=taxpayers)		**5–24 mill. €/a,** borne by the shippers
IWT	**ca. 2 mill. €/a,** mostly borne by society	na	na	na	**0.1–0.3 mill. €/a,** borne by the shippers
Short sea	**>10 mill. €/a,** mostly borne by society	na	na	na	**0.2–1 mill. €/a,** borne by the shippers
Aviation	na	**>0.7 bill. €/a**	na	na	**0.5–2.3 mill. €/a,** borne by the shippers
Light traffic (Mühlhausen 2011)	**>2 bill. €/a,** borne by the society and insurers	–	na	na	–
TOTAL	*>12 bill. €/a*	*>1.2 bill. €/a*	*ca. 1 bill. €/a*	*>0.3 bill. €/a*	*1–6 bill.€/a*
The EU-27 grand total for all modes and all cost items is at present more than 15 bill. euros p.a.					

Source: Nokkala et al., 2012.

Table 2.10. **WEATHER project's estimates on current extreme weather costs inside the EU**

Extreme weather event		Infrastructure Assets (m€)	Infrastructure Operations (m€)	Vehicle Assets (m€)	Vehicle Operations (m€)	User Time (m€)	Health & Life (m€)	Total (m€)
Storm	Road (1)	76,10	22,60	5,10	1,40	63,00	5,90	174,10
	Rail (2)	0,07		12,05		6,28		18,39
	Maritime (5)			2,10	17,98			20,08
	Intermodal (6) (7)	0,53					0,72	1,25
	Air (8)			53,80	34,30	38,40	28,30	154,80
Winter	Road (1)	248,80	126,30	81,30	12,50	125,50	164,90	759,30
	Rail (2) (3)	0,04		3,38		1,60		5,02
	Intermodal (6) (7)	0,21					0,21	0,42
	Air (8)		11,20	12,00	57,70	64,60	1,90	147,40
Flood	Road (1)	630,10	21,90	24,40	30,01	93,70	21,50	821,61
	IWW (4)					4,87		4,87
	Rail (2)	103,66		111,60		67,30		282,55
	Air (8)			3,20	26,50	29,60	0,20	59,50
	Intermodal (6) (7)	0,32					0,10	0,42
Heat&drought	Road (1)						46,90	46,90
Total		1059,82	182,00	308,92	180,39	494,84	270,63	2496,60

Notes: (1) Average year 2000-2010, (2) Average annual data 1999-2010, (3) Avalanches, winter storms and extreme heat events not included, (4) Average annual data 2003-2009, service providers' costs, (5) Average data hurricane Kyrill 2007 from case studies, freight transport, (6) Average data 2009 freight transport without AT, CH, I, CZ, DE (already included in rail), (7) Including extreme temperatures (heat), (8) Average annual data.
Source: Przyluski et al., 2011.

Figure 2.24. **Relative extreme weather indicators for EU-27**

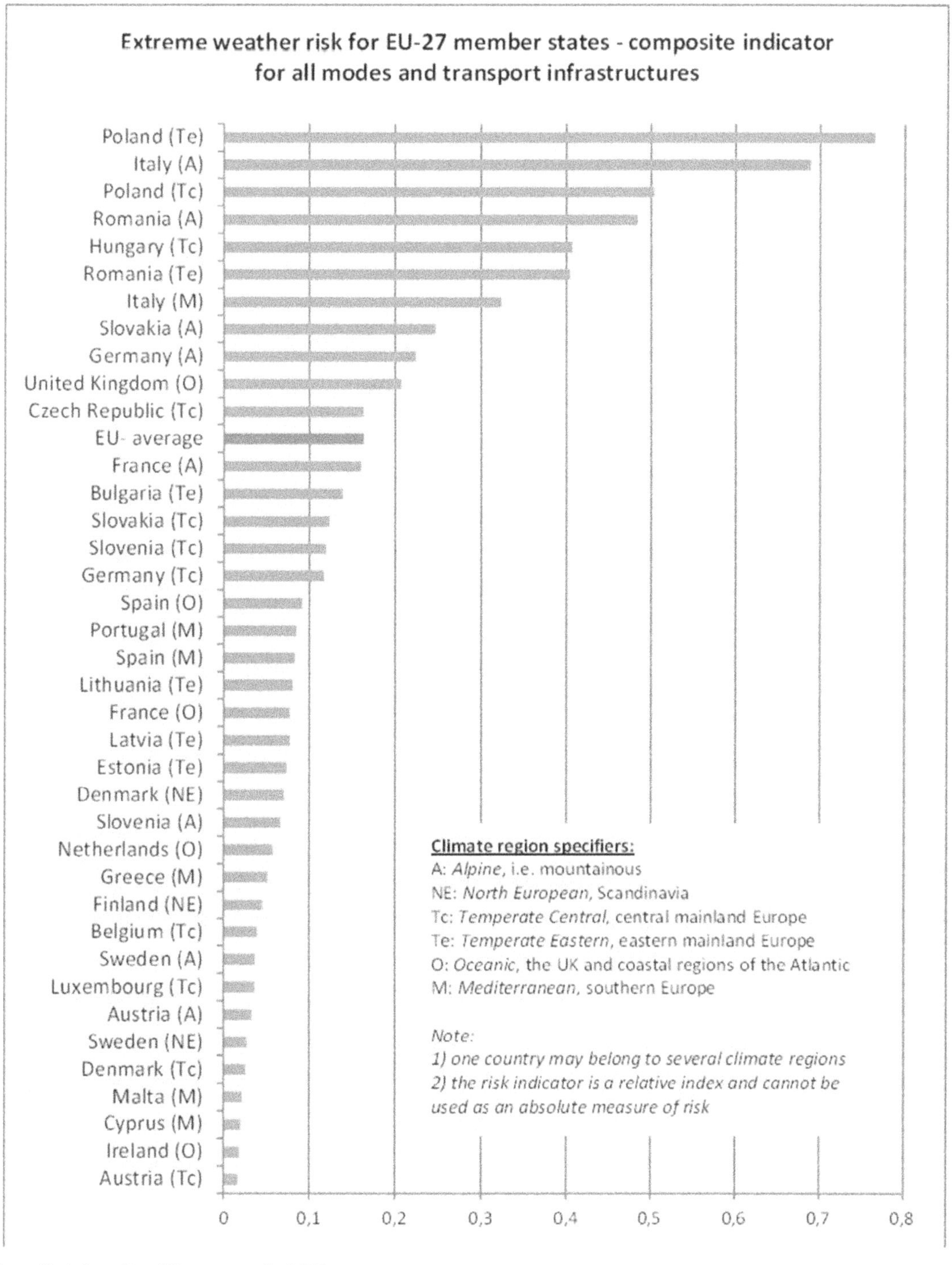

Source: Compiled from Leviäkangaset al., 2012.

According to the results from EWENT, different regions in Europe will respond to future changes in different ways, because the impacting weather phenomena and their future trends are different (Leviäkangas et al., 2011; Vajda et al., 2011). Furthermore, the aggregate statistics on transport systems and economic contexts combined with climatological data suggest that the risks in different EU member states deviate substantially from each other (Figure 2.24). Typically risks are concentrated to countries, regions and/or areas where:

- transport volume densities are high, which *de facto* means major urban centres and their surroundings as well as main transport corridors
- infrastructures are in poor technical condition and economic resources scarce to respond to/recover from extreme weather events
- weather phenomena can occur in their extreme form and can result in major economic losses.

As the risks are higher in some countries than in others, so will be the costs most likely; special focus is warranted in high-risk countries, regions and areas.

References

ABproTWE. Wikimedia Commons, licensed for use under CC BY 2.0.

Aursand, P. and I. Horvli (2009), "Effect of a changed climate on gravel roads" in E. Tutumluer, I. Al-Qadi (eds.) *Bearing capacity of roads, railways and airfields*. Taylor and Francis Group, London.

Auld, H, D. MacIver and J. Klaassen (2006), "Adaptation Options for Infrastructure Under Changing Climate Conditions", Environment Canada, Ottawa. http://publications.gc.ca/site/fra/9.573364/publication.html

Baglin, C. (2012), "Airport Climate Adaptation and Resilience: A Synthesis of Airport Practice". *ACRP Synthesis 33*, Transportation Research Board, Washington D.C.

Becker, A., M. Acciaro, R. Asariotis, E.Cabrera, L. Cretegny, P. Crist, M. Esteban, A, Mather, S. Messner, S. Naruse, A.K.Y. Ng, S. Rahmstorf, M. Savonis, D-W. Song, V. Stenek and A. Velegrakis (2013), "A Note on Climate Change Adaptation for Seaports: A challenge for global ports, a challenge for global society". *Climatic Change*, Vol. 120/4, pp. 683.

Bilodeau, J.P., G. Doré, P. Thiam and F. Drolet (2013), "Long-term Performance of Flexible Pavement Structures in a Changing Climate". Transport Association of Canada, Winnipeg.

Bobylev, M. (2009), Urban underground infrastructure and climate change: Opportunities and threats. Proceedings of the Fifth Urban Research Symposium 2009, Marseille, 28-30 June.

Borkovic, J., A. Nolet and M. Roorda, (2015), "Economic Vulnerability of Northern Canadian Mining to Winter Road Degradation Due to Climate Change". Transportation Research Board of the National Academy of Sciences, Washington D.C.

Burda, W. Wikimedia Commons, licensed under CC BY-SA 3.0. https://commons.wikimedia.org/wiki/File%3ADK1_koleiny.jpg

Carter, M. (2013), Australian Local Government Financial Reform - A Federal Perspective. Australian Centre of Excellence for Local Government.

Case, D. Wikimedia Commons, licensed under CC BY-SA 3.0. https://commons.wikimedia.org/wiki/File:Forge_Hill_Road_bridge_washout_after_Hurricane_Irene,_New_Windsor,_NY.jpg

CIRIA (Construction, Industry, Research and Information Association) (2009), "Whole-life Infrastructure Asset Management: Good practice guide for civil infrastructure". CIRIA Report C677, London.

City of Champaign-Urbana. Wikimedia Commons, licensed under CC BY-SA 2.0.

Clarke, L. www.geography.org.uk, licensed under CC BY-SA 2.0.

Climate Central, http://sealevel.climatecentral.org/

Cochran, I. (2009), "Climate Change Vulnerabilities and Adaptation Possibilities for Transport Infrastructures in France", Climate Report 18, Mission Climat de la Caisse des Dépôts.

Cook, W., P. Barr and M. Halling (2014), "Segregation of Bridge Failure Causes and Consequences". Transportation Research Board of the National Academy of Sciences, Washington D.C.

de Bruin, K., R. Dellink and S. Agrawala (2009), "Economic Aspects of Adaptation to Climate Change: Integrated Assessment Modelling of Adaptation Costs and Benefits", *OECD Environment Working Papers*, No. 6, OECD Publishing, Paris.
DOI: http://dx.doi.org/10.1787/225282538105

Dehn, M., G. Bürger, J. Buma and P. Gasparetto (2000), "Impact of Climate Change on Slope Stability Using Expanded Downscaling", *Engineering Geology*, Vol. 55/3, pp. 193-204.

DfT (UK Department for Transport) (2014), "Transport Resilience Review", London.

DfT (UK Department for Transport) (2013), "Action for Roads: A network for the 21st century". London.

Dunne, J., R. Stouffer and J. John (2013), "Reductions in Labour Capacity from Heat Stress Under Climate Warming". *Nature Climate Change*, Vol. 3.

ECCONET (2012), "Climate Change and Adaptation to Inland Waterways". Rotterdam.

EichhostUrda (2009), "Adapting Urban Transport to Climate Change". Sustainable Transport: A Sourcebook for Policy-Makers in Developing Cities, Module 5-F. Deutsche Gesellschaft Für Internationale Zusammenarbeit (GIZ) GMBH, Eschborn.

Eurocontrol (2013), Challenges of Growth 2013: Task 8, Climate Change Risk and Resilience.

FHWA (2013), Bridges and Structures: National Bridge Inventory.
https://www.fhwa.dot.gov/bridge/nbi/no10/yrblt13.cfm (accessed 15 September 2015).

Garnaut, R. (2008), *The Garnaut Climate Change Review*. Cambridge University Press, Melbourne.

Karl, T.R., J.M. Melillo and T.C. Peterson (eds.) (2009), *Global Climate Change Impacts in the United States*, Cambridge University Press.

Hall, K., et al. (2007), "Long-Life Concrete Pavements in Europe and Canada". Report FHWA-PL-07-027 prepared for the Federal Highway Administration, Alexandria.

Hallegate, S., C. Green, R.J. Nicholls and J. Corfee-Morlot (2013), "Future Flood Losses in Major Coastal Cities". *Nature Climate Change*, Vol. 3.

Hering, A. Wikimedia Commons, licensed under CC BY 3.0.
https://commons.wikimedia.org/wiki/File:Qew_bruecke_nf_beton_kaputt_23_von_46.jpg

HM Treasury (2012), The Stern Review on the Economics of Climate Change.
http://webarchive.nationalarchives.gov.uk/+/http://www.hm-treasury.gov.uk/sternreview_index.htm (accessed 27 November 2012).

HM Government (2011), "Climate Resilient Infrastructure: Preparing for a Changing Climate". Report presented to UK Parliament by the Secretary of the State for Environment, Food and Rural Affairs by the Command of Her Majesty. May 2011.

Inturri, G. and M. Ignaccolo (2011), "The role of transport in mitigation and adaptation to Climate change impacts in urban areas", in *Resilient Cities*. Springer. Netherlands.

ITF (2008), *Long-Life Surfaces for Busy Roads*, OECD Publishing, Paris. DOI: http://dx.doi.org/10.1787/9789282101209-en

Jonkeren, O., P. Rietveld, J. van Ommeren and A. te Linde (2013), "Climate Change and Economic Consequences for Inland Waterway Transport in Europe". *Regional Environment Change*, Vol. 14/3.

Jonkeren, O., B. Jourquin and P. Rietveld (2011), "Modal Split Effects of Climate Change: The effect of low water levels on the competitive position of inland waterway transport in the river Rhine area". *Transportation Research Part A*, Vol. 45/10.

Kalantari, Z. (2011), *Adaptation of Road Drainage Structures to Climate Change*. Royal Institute of Technology (KTH), Stockholm.

Kaufman, S., C. Qing, N. Levenson and M. Hanson (2012), "Transportation During and After Hurricane Sandy". Rudin Center for Transportation, NYU Wagner Graduate School of Public Service, New York City.

Keller, J.A., A. Armstrong, M. Flood and M. Meyer (2011), "An approach to addressing the impacts of climate variability on roadway and bridge design". Proceedings of the 90th Transportation Research Board Annual Meeting, Washington D.C.

KLIWAS (2015), Auswirkungen des Klimawandels auf Wasserstraßen und Schifffahrt in Deutschland: Abschlussbericht, Bundesministerium für Verkehr und digitale Infrastruktur, KLIWAS.

Koetse, M. and P. Rietveld (2009), "The impact of climate change and weather on transport: An overview of empirical findings." *Transportation Research: Part D*, Vol. 14.

Larsen P.H. et al. (2008), "Estimating Future Costs for Alaska Public Infrastructure at Risk from Climate Change". *Global Environmental Change*, Vol. 18.

Leviäkangas, P., A. Tuominen, R. Molarius and H. Kojo (eds.) (2011), "Extreme Weather Impacts on Transport Systems". EWENT Deliverable D1. *VTT Working Papers* No. 168. http://www.vtt.fi/inf/pdf/workingpapers/2011/W168.pdf.

Leviäkangas, P. et al. (2012), "D6 European Extreme Weather Risk Management – Needs, Opportunities, Costs and Recommendations". EWENT project deliverable, VTT, July 2012. http://ewent.vtt.fi/Deliverables/D6/Ewent_D6_SummaryReport_V07.pdfLi, Z. and P. Kaini (2007). "Optimal Investment Decision-Making for Highway Transportation Asset management Under Risk and Uncertainty", Report MRUTC 07-10, Midwest Regional University Transportation Center, Madison.

Lindgren, J., D.K. Jonsson and A. Carlsson-Kanyama (2009), "Climate Adaptation of Railways: Lessons from Sweden", *European Journal of Transport and Infrastructure Research*, Vol. 9/2, pp. 164-181.

Maibach, M. et al. (2008), *Handbook on estimation of external costs in the transport sector. Internalisation measures and policies for all external costs of transport (IMPACT)*. Version 1.1, Delft. http://ec.europa.eu/transport/sites/transport/files/themes/sustainable/doc/2008_costs_handbook.pdf

Mailer_diablo. Wikimedia Commons, licensed under CC BY-SA 3.0.

Meade, J.N. and D.W. Janisch (2003), "Pavement Type Determination Task Force Report". Report MnDOT/OM-PM-2003-01, Minnesota Department of Transportation, Maplewood.

Metropolitan Transportation Authority of the State of New York. Wikimedia Commons, licensed under CC BY 2.0.

Meyer, M. et al. (2014), *Climate Change, Extreme Weather Events and the Highway System: A Practitioner's Guide*, Transportation Research Board of the National Academies, Washington, D.C.

Meyer, M.D., E. Rowan, M.J. Savonis and A. Choate (2012), "Integrating Extreme Weather Risk into Transportation Asset Management." American Association of State Highway and Transportation Officials (AASHTO).

Middlemann, M. (ed.) (2007), "Natural Hazards in Australia: Identifying risk analysis requirements, *Geoscience Australia: Canberra.*Vol. 7.

MunichRe (2009). *Natural catastrophes 2008: Analyses, assessments, positions.* Australasia/Oceania Volume, MunichRe: Munich.

Murray, H. Wikimedia Commons, licensed under Creative Commons Public Domain, Public Domain Mark 1.0. https://commons.wikimedia.org/wiki/File:Damaged_bridge_from_flooding_in_Pakistan,_2010.JPG?uselang=fr

Natural Resources Canada, licensed under Creative Commons Public Domain, Public Domain Mark 1.0.

NCDOT Communications. Wikimedia Commons, licensed under CC BY-NC-SA 2.0

Nemry, F. and H. Demirel (2012), "Impacts of Climate Change on Transport: A focus on road and rail infrastructures". Joint Research Centre of the European Commission, Institute for Prospective Technical Studies. Report nr JRC72217; EUR 25553 EN.

New York City Metropolitan Transit Authority, licensed under CC BY 2.0.

Nguyen, M.N., X. Wang and C.H. Wand (2012), "A Reliability Assessment of Railway Rrack Buckling During an Extreme Heatwave. Proceedings of the Institution of Mechanical Engineers, Part F *Journal of Rail and Rapid Transit*, Vol. 226/5, pp. 513-517.

Nokkala, M., P. Leviäkangas and K. Oiva (eds.) (2012), "The Costs of Extreme Weather for the European Transport System". EWENT Project D4, Vtt Technology 36, VTT Technical Research Centre of Finland, Espoo.

Oregon Department of Transportation. Wikimedia Commons, licensed under CC BY-SA 2.0

Parriaux, A. (2012), "Vulnérabilité des Infrastructures Géotechniques au Changement Climatique et Mesures d'Adaptation Selon le Contexte Géographique", Association mondiale de la route, Paris.

Perrin, J. and C. Jhaveri (2004), "The Economic Costs of Culvert Failures". Transportation Research Board of the National Academy of Sciences, Washington D.C.

Polemio, M. and L. Lollino (2011), "Failure of Infrastructure Embankments Induced by Flooding and Seepage: A neglected source of hazard". *Natural Hazards and Earth System Sciences*, Vol. 11.

Przyluski, V. et al. (2002), "Weather Extremes: Assessment of Impacts on Transport Systems and Hazards for European Regions - Deliverable 1: Weather Trends and Economy-Wide Impacts". Version: 2.0 (unapproved revised draft), 19 January 2012, Fraunhofer.

Radomski, W. (2002), *Bridge Rehabilitation*. Warsaw University of Technology, Poland. Imperial College Press, London.

Refsdal, G. and R. Johansen (2008), "Pavement service life and other lives". Proceedings of the Joint Nordic/Baltic Symposium on Pavement design and Performance Indicators - How should pavement service life be increased?

Rozman, D. Wikimedia Commons, licensed under CC BY-SA 3.0.

Russel, H.G. (2004), "Concrete Bridge Deck Performance: A Synthesis of Highway Practice". NCHRP Synthesis 333, Transportation Research Board, Washington D.C.

Ryall, M.J., G.A.R. Parke and J.E. Harding (2000), *The Manual of Bridge Engineering*, Thomas Telford.

Samtani, N.C. and E.A. Nowatzki (2006) *Soils and Foundations Reference Manual* – Vol. I, National Highway Institute, U.S. Department of Transportation, Federal Highway Administration, Washington D.C.

Sanchez, A. et al. (2012), "Transport, in Climate Change, Impacts and Vulnerability in Europe 2012 - An indicator-based report". Section 4.6, EEA Report No 12/2012. European Environment Agency, Copenhagen.

Santillán, D., E. Salete and M. Toledo (2015), "A Methodology for the Assessment of the Effect of Climate Change on the Thermal-strain–stress Behaviour of Structures". *Engineering Structures*, Vol. 92.

Sawyer, D. (2014), *The Economic Implications of Climate Change on Transportation Assets: An analysis framework*, International Institute for Sustainable Development, Winnipeg.

Schall, J. et al. (2012), *Hydraulic Design of Highway Culverts*, Third Edition, U.S. Department of Transportation; Federal Highway Administration, Washington D.C.

Schiessl, P., C. Gehlen and G. Kapteina (2004), "Assessment and Service Life Updating of Existing Tunnels". First International Symposium on Safe & Reliable Tunnels: Innovative European Achievements, Prague.

Schweikert, A., P. Chinowsky, X. Espinet and M. Tarbert (2014), "Climate Change and Infrastructure Impacts: Comparing the impact on roads in ten countries through 2100". *Procedia Engineering*, Vol. 78.

Scott, H. et al. (2013), "Climate Change Guidelines for Ports". National Climate Change Adaptation Research Facility, Melbourne.

Seattle Municipal Archives. Wikimedia Commons, licensed under CC BY 2.0.

Simoner, M. et al. (2012), Overview of Infrastructure Adaptation Measures and Resulting Discharge Scenarios, Via Donnau and BfG.

Sohanghpurwala, A.A. (2006), "Manual on Service Life of Corrosion-Damaged Reinforced Concrete Bridge Superstructure Elements". NCHRP Report 558, Transportation Research Board, Washington D.C.

Stenek, V. et al. (2011), "Climate Risks and Business Ports". Terminal Marítimo Muelles el Bosque Cartagena, Columbia. International Finance Corporation, World Bank Group, Washington D.C.

Stephenson, S.R. (2016). "Access to Arctic Urban Areas in Flux: Opportunities and Uncertainties in Transport and Development", in Orttung, R.W., (ed.) *Sustaining Russia's Arctic Cities: Resource Politics, Migration, and Climate Change*. Berghahn, New York.

Stewart, M., X. Wang and M. Nguyen (2012), "Climate Change Adaptation for Corrosion Control of Concrete Infrastructure". *Structural Safety*, Vol. 35.

Stewart, M., X. Wang and M. Nguyen (2011), "Climate Change Impacts and Risk of Concrete Infrastructure Deterioration". *Engineering Structures*, Vol. 33/4.

Stipanovic, I. et al. (2015), "The risk of frost damage in porous asphalt: Experiences from the Netherlands". Compendium of Papers presented at the 2015 meeting of the TRB.

Stowell, D. Wikimedia Commons, licensed under CC BY-SA 2.0. https://commons.wikimedia.org/wiki/Category:Rail_transport_washouts#/media/File:Washout_at_Oldbury_Viaduct_-_geograph.org.uk_-_552051.jpg

Taylor, M. and M. Philp (2015), "Investigating the Impact of Maintenance Regimes on the Design Life of Road Pavements in a Changing Climate and the Implications for Transport Policy". *Transport Policy*, Vol. 41, pp. 117-135.

Tenbusch, A., B. Dorwart and A. Tenbusch (2013), "Failing Culverts – Structural Problems & Economic Considerations". Tenbusch and Associates, Lewisville.

Tenbusch, A., B. Dorwart and Tenbusch (2009), "Failing Culverts - The Geotechnical Perspective". Tenbusch and Associates, Lewisville.

Tserng, H., S. Yin and C. Chung (2009) "Maintenance Strategy for Bridge Components on the Basis of Performance." J. Perform. Constr. Facil., 10.1061/(ASCE)0887-3828. Vol. 23/4, pp. 234-243.

Updegrave, C. Wikimedia Commons, licensed for use under CC BY 2.0. https://commons.wikimedia.org/wiki/File:Salmonberry_River_and_POTB_line.jpg

Vajda, A. et al. (2011), "Probabilities of adverse weather affecting transport in Europe: climatology and scenarios up to the 2050s". Report No. 2011:9, Finnish Meteorological Institute, Helsinki. https://helda.helsinki.fi/ handle/10138/28592.

Visitor7. Wikimedia Commons, licensed under CC BY-SA 3.0. https://commons.wikimedia.org/wiki/File:Oregon_Coast_Highway_Washout.jpg

Wang, X. et al. (2011), "Analysis of Climate Change Impacts on the Deterioration of Concrete Infrastructure - Part 1: Mechanisms, Practices, Modelling and Simulations – A review", Commonwealth Scientific and Industrial Research Organisation (CSIRO), Canberra, Vol. 41.

World Bank (2012), "4° Turn Down the Heat – Why a 4°C Warmer World Must be Avoided". A report for the World Bank by the Potsdam Institute for Climate Impact Research and Climate Analysis.

Wright, L. et al. (2012), "Estimated Effects of Climate Change on Flood Vulnerability of U.S. Bridges". *Mitigation and Adaptation Strategies for Global Change* Vol. 17/8.

Willway, T., S. Reeves and L. Baldachin (2008), "Maintaining Pavements in a Changing Climate". Report commissioned by the Department for Transport, The Stationery Office, London.

Notes

1 Or climate-related variables in the case of sea level rise.

2 Scouring refers to the removal of sediment from around *bridge abutments* or piers which are the result of moving water; this process may compromise the structural integrity of a bridge.

3 The following section draws on Youman (2007); Willway et al. (2008); Meyer et al. (2014); Nemry and Demirel (2012).

4 For a description of RCP scenarios, see Chapter 1.

5 Quantity of water in the soil.

6 Forces keeping a collection of particles (for example soil, sand or gravel) together.

7 Such as the "Rational method" (Meyer et al., 2014; Kalantari, 2011) or "Critical storm duration".

8 Rail segments welded together into a single rail of a length of several kilometres.

9 It is noteworthy that the definition of extremes strongly varied between approaches. In both projects it had to be acknowledged that there is a lack of reliable statistical data for a sound cost assessment. For more information, see EWENT (http://ewent.vtt.fi/) and WEATHER (http://www.weather-project.eu/weather/index.php).

Chapter 3. Adaptation frameworks for transport infrastructure: Linking vulnerability assessment, risk management and performance objectives

Prioritising dependable, robust and resilient network connectivity as the reference performance criteria for infrastructure adaptation policies ensures that these policies consistently enable and preserve the core benefits delivered by infrastructure assets. This chapter outlines how transport infrastructure owners and network managers can embed network access and connectivity performance into their asset management policies. This chapter also describes climate change adaptation frameworks for transport authorities and asset owners. It discusses, in essence, the question of "How to prepare to adapt?" Having a coherent framework for adaptation policies can go far to ensure that risks are highlighted, responsibilities allocated, interventions are prioritised and that strategic decisions are not overlooked.

Transportation networks and assets are basic infrastructure that facilitate social and economic activity and as such they form a vital resource that is expected to be operational at all times. Managing these assets effectively is of critical importance for all transport agencies and infrastructure managers because:

- Networks and associated infrastructure are vital links in providing access and mobility for communities and industry.
- The value of transport infrastructure assets for all classes of roads is very high compared to other public infrastructure. For example, Austroads (2009a) indicates that the road networks of Australia and New Zealand may be valued at about AUS 150 billion dollars in replacement cost terms, which equates to approximately 50% of the total government capital investment in education, health, energy, mining and manufacturing combined in those two countries.
- Effective stewardship is essential to help ensure public safety, for retaining the value and serviceability of these assets for future generations, and for providing best value to users and investors, noting that transportation networks and assets commonly have expected engineering lives of many decades.
- Communities and their governments are demanding increased accountability for effective and efficient spending of public funds.
- Competition for limited funds across government and other sectors is increasing.

Given that the transport system is a vital community asset which provides the platform for transport and communication, it thus forms an essential component of the social and economic life of a society. As indicated in Figure 3.1, community benefits (such as economic growth, social activity, etc.) are achieved fully or in part through the performance of the transport system (providing access, mobility, efficient travel and transport, etc.). This figure also illustrates the key elements of asset management for road networks. All elements are interrelated.[1]

Figure 3.1. **Elements of an asset management system for road networks**

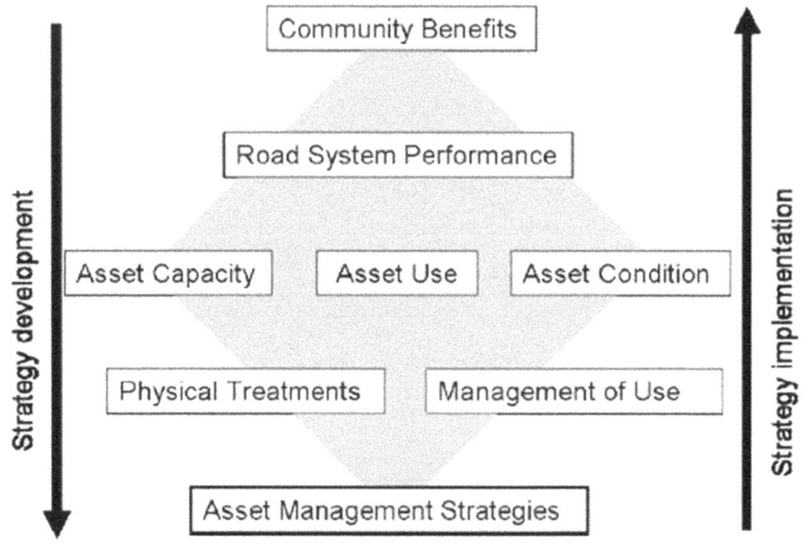

Source: Austroads, 2009b.

Performance assessment

The performance of a transport system is achieved through the integrated management of the capacity, condition, and use of the assets. Such characteristics are affected by a combination of physical treatments (construction/maintenance) to manage and maintain assets, together with operational measures to manage how the system is used and the vehicles and people that have access to the network. The transport agency is responsible and accountable for the management and stewardship of the transport system to ensure an acceptable, affordable and sustainable level of performance appropriate to its many uses. Most agencies therefore adopt a set of performance indicators for use in monitoring the operational states and trends in their systems.

Austroads (2009b) recommends that a set of indicators should be developed and applied which enables assessment of the effectiveness of achievements relative to the outcomes sought, and the efficiency of the inputs used to achieve such outcomes. Austroads' indicators are tailored to roads but an analogous list can be derived for other transport modes and services. These indicators should be:

- relevant to the strategy objectives
- simple to compile and monitor
- based upon data of suitable quality normally collected by the road agency for asset management
- transparent and meaningful to stakeholders
- representative of the total asset
- sensitive to detectible changes in the asset and its use
- a catalyst for sound asset investment decisions and management practice.

The performance indicators shown in Table 3.1 provide typical examples of key performance indicators pertaining to the asset management system elements identified in Figure 3.1.

From Table 3.1 and Figure 3.1 together the following results can be drawn:

1. The key result areas (KRA) for a road system management (RSM) strategy are the economic, social and environmental outcomes sought by the community. The key performance indicators (KPI) for the RSM strategy are the measures of the aspects of road system performance which affect those outcomes (KRAs). The KPIs are derived in turn from data on the attributes of road system condition, capacity and use. The RSM strategy sets target for these attributes for the various parts of the road system.
2. The road investment strategy (RIS), the infrastructure preservation strategy (IPS) and the road use management (RUM) strategies guide the management of road system capacity, condition and use respectively in accordance with the target standards established in the road system management strategy.
3. The KPIs for the outputs of the RIS, IPS and RUMs are the extent to which the respective target attributes of the road system are achieved (e.g. km of duplicated road).
4. The KPIs for the efficiency of implementation of the RIS, IPS and RUMs are the extent to which the respective targets are achieved for a given level of resource input (e.g. cost per km of duplication).

5. The KPIs for the effectiveness of the RIS, IPS and RUMs are the extent to which the implementation achieves outcomes relevant to the KRAs for the given level of resource input (e.g. economic BCR).

Table 3.1. **Typical key result areas and key performance indicators for road system asset management**

Element of transport asset management system	Key result areas (KRA)	Key performance indicators (KPI)
Community benefits	Economic development Mobility, safety and accessibility Sustainable environmental management	
Road system performance		User satisfaction Travel speed User cost Congestion Lane occupancy rate Casualty crashes Variability of travel time Ride quality Greenhouse gas emissions
Asset capacity		Network length Network connectivity % network by road type and lane widths % network by surface type Mass and height capacity of routes
Asset use		Traffic volumes by road user and vehicle types Distances travelled Extent of access for all road user and vehicle types Tonne-km of road freight Number and severity of crashes Noise and air pollutant emissions
Asset condition		Pavement roughness, rutting and cracking Skid resistance Bridge load capacity Effective height and width clearances Condition of drainage systems Condition of roadside vegetation
Physical treatments		Return on construction expenditure "Triple bottom line" assessment of programs Economic return of individual project BCRs Life cycle costs of maintenance regime
Management of use		BCR of traffic management projects % signal downtime Compliance with designated lane use

Source: Austroads, 2009b.

Role of planning

In the likelihood that climate change alters the biophysical environment and impacts the environmental serviceability of urban systems, planning principles and practice will play an important and complementary role in adaptation to climate change in addition to the design, maintenance and operation of transport infrastructure. Land use planning can provide a powerful tool to help reduce the loss of life, property, and assets. While planning can be especially helpful in keeping population and assets away from vulnerable zones, the general tendency has been for further concentration of population and infrastructure in these zones – and in particular in vulnerable coastal areas (Auld et al., 2006; MunichRe, 2010). Nonetheless, efficient and proactive planning can mitigate the threat of climate change impacts to transportation systems can be minimised by separating infrastructure and the associated population and resources in high risk areas such as floodplains and coastal zones threatened by inundation.

Brown et al. (1997) provided an example of efficient planning to reduce the impact of flooding associated with extreme storm events. This study compared the impacts from storm events in Michigan, US, and adjacent Ontario, Canada. The comparison found that non-agricultural flood damage in Michigan exceeded the damage in Ontario by a factor of approximately 900, despite the fact that the flood magnitudes experienced in Ontario were greater than Michigan. Further analysis revealed that this was due to the differences in land use planning systems applied in the two jurisdictions, where Michigan had a lower design threshold for residential development in flood prone areas. This example demonstrates how land use planning can significantly reduce the impact and damages related to climate change, and how planning systems may need to evolve in response to climate change (as well as concurrent changes in demographic and settlement patterns).

Role of liability and insurance

The increasing frequency and severity of extreme climate events impacting land-based transport infrastructure has the potential to produce a corresponding increase in the risk of potential accidents involving property damage, injuries and fatalities (CSIRO, 2006; Middlemann, 2007; Garnaut, 2008). This impact will in turn increase the potential liability and insurance costs to transport authorities, managers, operators and owners.

CSIRO (2006) conducted an infrastructure and climate change risk assessment for the state of Victoria, Australia, and determined that "it is the ultimate owner of any piece of infrastructure who must ensure that it is designed to operate effectively for its design life, since they will bear the primary liability in the event of failure". This study also found that many of the risks identified for land-based transport infrastructure are covered under existing insurance arrangements. Insurance and financial markets disperse the risks of climate change impacts across a wide base of industries, communities, regions, and countries, moderating the losses experienced by particular groups of people (Garnaut, 2008). The dilemma lies in the likelihood that as the understanding and occurrence of climate change impacts increases, insurers may act to reduce their potential exposure through limitations in event coverage. If insurance claims greatly increase as a result of severe weather events, then highly correlated risks across regions may overwhelm the ability for the industry to provide insurance coverage (Garnaut, 2008). Land use planning mechanisms as described under the "adaptation planning" subsection of this chapter may act to improve insurability and minimise pressure on the insurance sector.

Accounting for user behaviour

There also exists the potential for climate change to impact the way people use transportation infrastructure with shifts in demand in response to climate factors, and in their travel behaviour. Climate change may result in shifts in demographics as currently populated areas become less desirable, changes in tourism markets and production and industries shift according to the impacts of climate change, such as excessive heat or coastal inundation (USDOT, 2002; TRB, 2008; Koetse and Rietveld, 2009). These shifts in turn have implications on transport demand and patterns, infrastructure maintenance and operation on a local, regional and global scale.

Travel behaviour also varies according to weather conditions. Research has revealed that an overall reduction in traffic volume in Melbourne, Australia, of 2-3% occurs in response to 2-10 mm of rain during daytime, with reductions in spring somewhat larger than those in winter (Keay and Simmonds, 2005). Increased extreme precipitation events therefore may periodically increase pressure on alternative transport modes. Adverse weather conditions are also a recognised risk factor known to affect crash rates (e.g. Rowland et al., 2007; Koetse and Rietveld, 2009). Rain and wet road conditions have been found to be significant contributors to road fatalities and crashes as a percentage of the total road toll in Australia (Rowland et al., 2007). This correlation suggests that the changes in driver behaviour under adverse conditions are insufficient to account for the resultant hazards such as reduced road/tyre friction, loss of vehicle control and poor visibility (Edwards, 1999; Unrau and Andrey, 2006). Koetse and Rietveld (2009) summarised that adverse weather conditions resulted in substantial reductions in traffic speed, travel time and travel time reliability. Stern and Zehavi (1990) also found substantially increased risk of a crash, particularly in single vehicle crashes, under heat stress conditions induced by extremely hot days and heat waves. The increased risk for bushfires may also alter driver behaviour due to a reduction of visibility because of smoke (TRB, 2008). Driver education and increased deployment of advisory systems have the potential to provide an adaptation mechanism for user behaviour in the changing climate conditions.

Emergency evacuation, transport network and vehicle function

Climate change may affect the function of traffic systems by reducing traffic speed and volume, increasing travel time delay, and decreasing roadway capacity. The functioning of traffic systems will be further hampered by the impact of climate change conditions on the efficiency and functioning of vehicles. Increased temperatures are predicted to result in more vehicle overheating and breakdowns, and lead to faster tyre deterioration resulting in blow outs, thereby further increasing traffic disruptions (TRB, 2008; Evans et al., 2009; Jaroszweski et al., 2010).

Predicted increases in hot days and heat waves attributed to climate change are likely to impact on vehicle efficiencies. Warming conditions can lower engine efficiency resulting in increasing fuel use, which is amplified further by the increased use of air conditioning in vehicles (TRB, 2008; Evans et al., 2009).

A robust transport network is required to offer alternative travel paths to ensure the effective functioning of systems. In most urban settings plentiful alternative routes exist due to the density of the road network and in many instances due to the presence of fixed-route public transport. In rural settings, however, road networks are sparser with fewer good quality alternative roads. The failure of one particular link within a rural road network potentially has significant effects on the community (Sohn, 2006; Jenelius et al., 2006; Taylor and Susilawati, 2012).

A robust transport network is essential in order to accommodate emergency services and planning particularly with respect to emergency evacuations. The increasing occurrence and severity of extreme weather events including cyclones, coastal inundation, bushfires and floods may result in the increased frequency of evacuation potentially over larger areas, with risks exacerbated by increasing populations in exurban areas, and especially in coastal zones. In the past there has been little research focussed on increasing the efficiency of evacuation due to the low demand for evacuations and the perception that the evacuation of a major city would create demands that would overwhelm the capacity of transport infrastructure (Wolshon and Meehan, 2003). Past and present practice has tended to disregard evacuation considerations in transport planning, design and analysis.

In 1999, Hurricane Floyd triggered the then third largest evacuation in US history when 2.6 million coastal residents of five states were evacuated as the hurricane approached (Wolshon and Meehan, 2003). The issues that emerged during this evacuation highlighted the importance of improving evacuation operation, and since there has been increased emergency evacuation research and planning in the US (e.g. Fu and Wilmot, 2004). The experiences from Hurricane Katrina subsequently suggested that much remains to be done (e.g. Litman, 2006; Lindell and Prater, 2007). Research on transport implications remains limited. Wolshon and Meehan (2003) summarised some of the practices that can be applied to traffic systems to increase evacuation efficiency:

- Contraflow strategies, where lanes and shoulders are reversed to increase conveyance in the dominant direction, have been shown to potentially increase the outbound volume by approximately 70%. Similar strategies can also be applied to assist in maximising evacuation flow including co-ordination of traffic signals on parallel arterial roads, use of public transport systems especially to assist low mobility community members, and limiting interruptions to flow at rail crossings and drawbridges.
- Deployment of intelligent transportation systems in urban areas, and supplementary advisory services to assist rural areas in order to inform drivers of the most efficient evacuation routes as conditions change.
- Removing any limitations imposed in road work areas to minimise delays.

Vulnerability assessment of transport networks

In broad terms, network vulnerability deals with the socio-economic impacts and transport systems performance of degraded transport networks. Thus network vulnerability is not just an interesting topic for research by transport network modellers; it is also of great importance to decision-makers and society at large. Degraded network performance from system failures, disaster situations or even traffic congestion can have significant social and economic impacts. Network failures, whether full or partial or whether due to natural or man-made events, are of great significance. These failures can range from disasters such as earthquakes and bridge collapses, whose effects may persist for long periods of time, to incident-based congestion episodes of relatively short duration but which still with large social and economic impacts. The climate change impacts outlined in Chapter 2 of this report all have the potential to contribute to complex system failures that can significantly degrade transport network performance. Transport agencies require well-defined concepts and validated models and tools to test networks for their robustness and resilience to failure at different locations, as an integral part of network design and incident management planning, including planning for emergencies.

Considerations of critical infrastructure are now a major concern in many countries (Murray and Grubesic, 2007). The concern stems from a variety of causes, including the state of development, condition and level of use of existing infrastructure systems, especially transport networks; difficulties associated with public sector provision of new infrastructure; public-private partnership arrangements for infrastructure provision; and perceptions of risks and threats to infrastructure from both natural disasters (e.g. floods, fire or earthquake) and from human malevolence such as acts of sabotage, war or terrorism. By way of example, the Australian Federal Government has defined critical infrastructure as "that infrastructure which if destroyed, degraded or rendered unavailable for an extended period, will significantly impact on social or economic well-being or affect national security or defence" (Attorney-

General's Department, 2003). A pertinent question is then how to identify critical locations in an infrastructure network. For example, the road transport network is large, wide and diverse in nature. Are there particular locations or facilities in that network where loss or degradation of certain road sections (links) will have significant impacts? How should such impacts be assessed? Thus there are needs for the development and application of a methodology to assess risk and vulnerability of transport networks. Methods and decision support tools are needed that allow planners and policy makers to make rational assessments of threats to facilities and infrastructure; the consequences of network degradation and failure at various locations and under different circumstances; and what to do about these. Social and economic benefits flow from the ability to plan for and manage the impacts of transport network degradation to minimise wider consequences on economic, employment, trade and social activities in cities and regions.

This section provides an overview of recent research on the development of methodologies for transport network vulnerability analysis, based on considerations of the socio-economic impacts of network degradation. At one level this involves considerations of alternative paths through a network and the relative probabilities of use of those paths. Whilst probability of use is important in defining potential weak spots in a network, this probability is not of itself a complete measure of vulnerability – the most critical locations in a network will show the most severe (socio-economic) consequences resulting from network failure at those locations. The methods therefore consider vulnerability assessment in terms of a planning systems process in which the performance of network components is tested against established performance criteria. The risks and consequences associated with failures at different locations need to be accounted for. Suitable metrics that may be used to interpret the extent and consequence of network failure or degradation need to be developed and tested.

The concept of network vulnerability is relatively new, and it is important to define what is meant by vulnerability. For instance, there are several possible responses to the reduced performance of a degraded network, or in dealing with the perceived risks of degradation at different locations. In some cases, an appropriate response may be to upgrade key transport infrastructure, for instance by raising it above expected maximum flood levels or by adding more capacity. But sometimes this simply makes the network more reliant on those key links and more vulnerable to their failure. An alternative approach is to add links to the network. These links may normally be redundant but provide alternative routes when key network links are broken. At the urban network level there may already be many such latent alternative routes, but at the regional or national strategic network level this is less likely to be the case. Extra links would make the transport network more robust, but this may add unnecessary cost to the provision of transport infrastructure. In other cases, the decision may be to focus not on hard protection of assets but rather on safe failure modes and rapid recovery of network performance. The question is where are these locations of potential network vulnerability and what is the best response. The starting point for study of network vulnerability is the study of transport network reliability, which has been the subject of intense international research interest since the Kobe earthquake of 1995.

Network reliability

Transport network reliability has been the subject of considerable international research interest in recent years (Lam, 1999; Bell and Cassir, 2000; Iida and Bell, 2003; FHWA, 2006; ITF, 2010). Much of this research has focused on congested urban road networks and the probability that a network will deliver a required standard of performance. The urban studies are important, but they are not the only areas of concern, especially when considering the wider implications of transport systems performance. At the regional and national strategic level, accessibility, regional coverage and inter-urban connectivity are the primary considerations. In these sparse networks, "vulnerability" of the network can be more important than "reliability" because of the potentially severe adverse consequences of network degradation. As noted by the Australian Bureau of Transport and Regional Economics (BTRE, 2002) in its analysis of the effects of flooding on road access, "the vast distances involved means that access to alternative services (such as hospitals and business) often do not exist...disruption costs to households, businesses and communities can therefore be more important in rural and remote communities". In both urban and rural areas, the concept of vulnerability or incident audit – the proactive determination of locations in a transport network that may be most sensitive to failure and where network failure may have the gravest consequences – requires detailed research. The transport planner may seek opportunities to reduce vulnerability and the community will demand such action.

Network reliability became an important research topic in transport planning during the 1990s, although some elements had been the subject of research interest for some time before that (e.g. Lee, 1946; Herman and Lam, 1974; Richardson and Taylor, 1978; Taylor, 1982). The Kobe earthquake of 1995 and its aftermath stimulated an interest in connectivity reliability. This is the probability that a pair of nodes in a network remains connected – i.e. there continues to exist a connected path between them – when one or more links in the network have been cut. Bell and Iida (1997) provided an analytical procedure for assessing connectivity reliability, and a summary of the procedure is given by Iida (1999). Subsequent research was directed at degraded networks, usually urban road networks subject to traffic congestion, in which the network remained physically intact but the performance of one or more links could be so severely affected by congestion that their use by traffic is curtailed. This led to the definition of two additional forms of reliability: travel time reliability and capacity reliability.

Travel time reliability considers the probability that a trip between an origin-destination pair can be completed successfully within a specified time interval (Bell and Iida, 1997). This can be affected by fluctuating link flows and imperfect knowledge of drivers when making route choice decisions (Lam and Xu, 2000). One measure of link travel time variability is the coefficient of variation of the distribution of individual travel times (Bates et al., 2001). Measures of travel time variability are useful in assessing network performance in terms of service quality provided to travellers on a day-to-day basis (FHWA, 2006). Thus travel time variability can be seen as a measure of demand satisfaction under congested conditions (Asakura, 1999).

A supply-side measure of network performance in congested networks is capacity reliability (Yang, Lo and Tang, 2000). Capacity reliability is defined as the probability that a network can successfully accommodate a given level of travel demand. The network may be in its normal state or in a degraded stated (say due to incidents or road works). Chen, Lo, Yang and Tang (1999) defined this probability as equal to the probability that the reserve capacity of the network is greater than or equal to the required demand for a given capacity loss due to degradation. Yang, Lo and Tang (2000) indicated that capacity reliability and travel time reliability together could provide a valuable transport network design tool. Taylor (1999; 2000) demonstrated how the concepts of travel time reliability and capacity reliability could be used in planning and evaluating traffic management schemes in an urban area.

Further research on network reliability is required to develop these concepts into practical traffic planning tools. In addition, there is a need for further research to properly specify travellers' responses to uncertainty (Bonsall, 2000), so that reliability research can be used to properly inform developments of new driver information systems and to influence the design of traffic control systems.

Network vulnerability

The discussion above suggests that the standard approaches to transport network reliability have focused on network connectivity and travel time and capacity reliability. While this provides valuable insights into certain aspects of network performance, reliability arguments based on probabilities and absolute connectivity may obscure potential network problems, especially in large-scale, sparse regional or national networks. In these networks the consequences of a disruption or degradation of the network become important.

For example, D'Este and Taylor (2001) used the extreme example of the Australian national strategic land transport system to illustrate the potential consequences of the severance of certain transport connections in this multimodal network. In this example the system reliability was considered, in terms of a cut to the Eyre Highway and transcontinental rail line on the Nullarbor Plain between Perth and Adelaide, for instance by flood (a perfectly plausible scenario), see Figure 3.2. The overall network remains connected and the probability that the route in question is cut by flood or other natural cause is very small (but not zero, for it has happened), so the travel time and capacity reliabilities are high. Therefore the established measures of network reliability discussed above would not indicate any major problem with the network. However the consequences of network failure are substantial in real terms – in this case the next best feasible path through the network involves a detour of some 5 000 km. In reality the alternative route via Broome would not be used – it is more likely that shipments would be delayed or cancelled thereby producing a different but no less significant economic impact. Nicholson and Dalziell (2003) pointed to similar circumstances in their study of the regional highway network in the centre of the North Island of New Zealand, a region subject to both snowstorms and volcanic eruptions.

Figure 3.2. **Effect of a loss of connectivity in the Australian National Highway System (NHS) network**

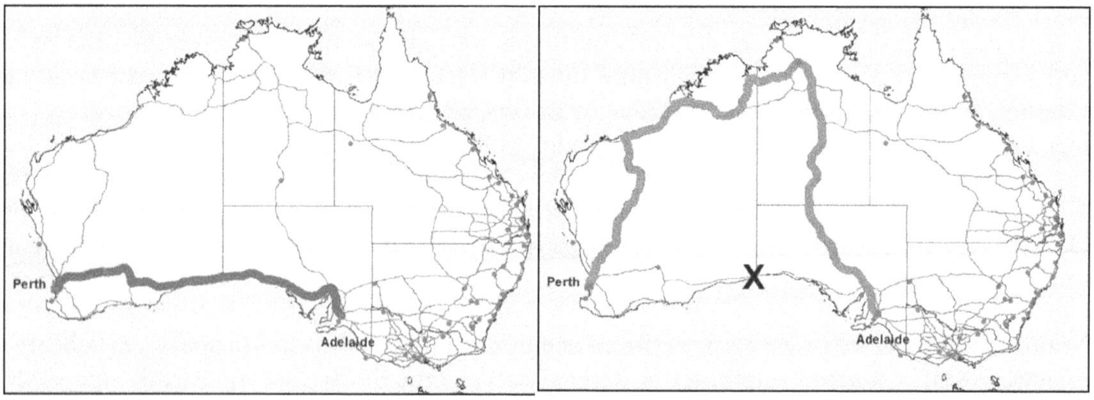

Note: Shortest path from Perth to Adelaide in full network (left) and network with Eyre Highway cut (right).
Source: D'Este and Taylor, 2001.

These examples illustrate the concept of network vulnerability and the difference between network reliability and vulnerability. The concept of vulnerability is more strongly related to the consequences of link failure, irrespective of the probability of failure. In some cases, link failure may be statistically unlikely but the resulting adverse social and economic impacts on the community may be sufficiently large to indicate a major problem warranting remedial action – akin to taking out an insurance policy for an extremely unlikely yet potentially catastrophic event. For example, consider the impact on a rural community of loss of access to markets for its produce and to vital human services (such as a hospital). Low probability of occurrence and network performance elsewhere does not offset the consequences of a network failure. Thus network reliability and vulnerability are related concepts but while reliability focuses on connectivity and probability, vulnerability is more closely aligned with network weakness and consequences of failure. Berdica (2002) proposed that vulnerability analysis of transport networks should be regarded as an overall framework through which different transport studies could be conducted to determine how well a transport system would perform when exposed to different kinds and intensities of disturbances. From her study of the road network in central Stockholm she suggested three main questions that might be posed in these studies:

1. How do interruptions of different critical links affect system performance, and to what extent?
2. How is network performance affected by general capacity reductions and possible changes to traffic management and road space allocation in a sub-region of the network?
3. How is the system affected by variations in travel demand?

These questions provide a starting point for the development of a methodology for study of vulnerability in transport networks and infrastructure. They highlight the key issue of the identification of critical components of the networks. Vulnerability analysis is intended to address these questions and the perhaps more important questions that flow from them – when the vulnerable elements (the "weakest links") of a transport network have been identified, what is the best response and what can be done about it?

Vulnerability and risk

Vulnerability, reliability and risk are closely linked concepts. In broad terms, risk is something associated with negative outcomes for life, health, or economic or environmental condition. Risk can be defined in many different ways, but most definitions focus on two factors: the probability that an event with negative impacts will occur, and the extent and severity of the resultant consequences of that event. Commonly, the product of probability and a measure of consequence is used as an index of risk. This may be shown schematically as a "risk matrix", as in Figure 3.3.

Figure 3.3. **Conceptual risk matrix**

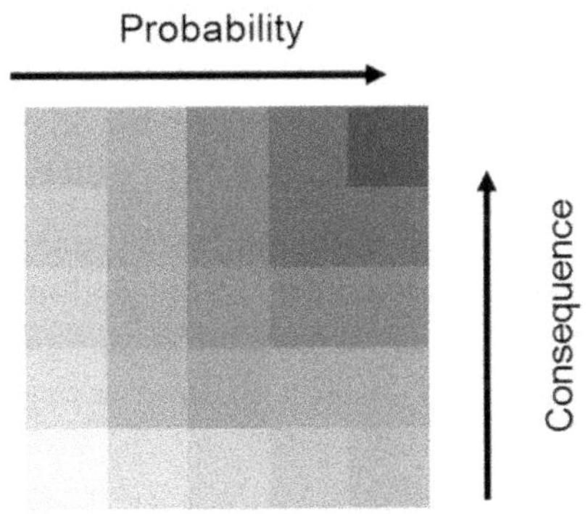

Risk and reliability analysis is mostly concerned with the top-right sector of the matrix where increasing probability and increasing consequences combine. Nicholson and Dalziell (2003) applied this framework to the risk assessment of transport networks in New Zealand. They measured risk as simply the sum of the products of the event probabilities and the economic costs of the event (e.g. the expected annual economic cost of a given event). Their risk evaluation process involved the following steps:

1. establish the context (i.e. the technical, financial, legal, social and other criteria for assessing the acceptability of risk)
2. identify the hazards (i.e. the potential causes of closure)
3. analyse the risks (i.e. identify the probabilities, consequences and expectations)
4. assess the risks (i.e. decide which risks are acceptable and which are unacceptable).

If any risk is found unacceptable, it needs to be managed. This generally involves either treating the unacceptable risks, using the most cost-effective treatment options, or monitoring and reviewing the risks (i.e. evaluating and revising treatments).

The study of vulnerability extends this risk assessment framework in several important ways. Firstly it extends the region of interest to areas of high consequences and low or unquantifiable (but non-zero) probability of occurrence – on the basis that measurement of occurrence probability and consequences (human and economic) is imprecise for many types of incidents, and society may well consider some consequences to be unacceptable and worthy of safeguarding against, despite uncertainty about their probability of occurrence (e.g. Evans, 1994). Secondly, vulnerability analysis provides a framework for targeting risk assessment. One of the key conclusions of the Nicholson-Dalziell risk assessment of the New Zealand highway network was that it is impractical and financially infeasible to conduct detailed geophysical and other risk assessment across an entire transport network. The costs of deriving accurate location-specific risk probabilities across a range of risk factors are too high to make it viable – what is needed is a way of targeting risk assessment resources to get the best value from them. Vulnerability analysis provides another way of approaching this problem. It can be used to find structural weaknesses in the network topology that render the network vulnerable to consequences of failure or degradation. Resources can then be targeted at assessing these "weak links". Thirdly, vulnerability auditing admits a more proactive and targeted approach to the issue of transport network risk assessment and mitigation.

Accessibility in the context of vulnerability assessment: Definitions

Transport network vulnerability owes its origins to Berdica (2002) and D'Este and Taylor (2003). For Berdica, vulnerability was "a susceptibility to incidents that can result in considerable reductions in road network serviceability". Serviceability itself related to nodes and links in a road network, and was defined as the possibility to use that link/route/road network during a given time period. This general notion of vulnerability continues in widespread use, see for instance Berdica and Mattsson (2007), Jenelius, Petersen and Mattsson (2006) and Jenelius and Mattsson (2012).

D'Este and Taylor (2001; 2003) defined vulnerability by using the notion of accessibility, i.e. the ease by which individuals from specific locations in a region may participate in activities (e.g. employment, education, shopping, trade and commerce) that take place in other physical locations in and around the region and by using a transport system to gain access to those locations. Then transport network vulnerability is defined in the following terms:

- A network node is vulnerable if loss (or substantial degradation) of a small number of links significantly diminishes the accessibility of the node, as measured by a standard index of accessibility.
- A network link is critical if loss (or substantial degradation) of the link significantly diminishes the accessibility of the network or of particular nodes, as measured by a standard index of accessibility.

This definition requires the use of an accessibility metric that is sensitive to network topology and network operating conditions.

Thus there are two alternative definitions in use for transport network vulnerability. Each has its own field of application. Berdica's serviceability definition is useful for considering "short term" (hours – days) disruptions, degradations and failures in a network. It is also concerned with network operations and the effects on those of network degradation. Serviceability may also be seen as a supply-side view of vulnerability. The D'Este-Taylor definition is useful for more long term (weeks – months) disruptions, degradations and network failures. It is primarily concerned with the wider socio-economic impacts of network degradation, and may be seen as a demand-side view of vulnerability. The following sections first consider accessibility-based vulnerability analysis, and then serviceability-based vulnerability.

Accessibility concepts

The notion of accessibility in transportation planning can be illustrated through a basic definition: accessibility is the ease with which desired destinations may be reached (Niemeier, 1997). For particular circumstances, this broad definition may be refined to explicitly include other relevant factors, such as time dependency which may be an issue in, for instance, assessing accessibility levels for public transport users where the level of service of public transport provision varies widely over hours of the day or days of the week. Thus Primerano and Taylor (2005) defined accessibility as "the ease for people to participate in activities from specific locations to a destination using a mode of transport at a specific time". In a similar vein, Chen et al. (2007) defined accessibility as "the quantification of an individual's freedom to participate in activities in the environment".

In regional and rural areas the basic definition for accessibility is appropriate but given the reliance on the road network as the infrastructure system providing mobility in these areas, the definition may be refined to indicate that accessibility is the ease with which services and facilities can be reached while using the road network. Alternatively, given the typical sparseness of regional road networks and the dispersed population in rural or remote regions, it may be more useful to consider the inverse of accessibility, which may be termed remoteness.

While a number of alternative metrics for accessibility are available (e.g. Sohn, 2006; Chen et al., 2007; Taylor and Susilawati, 2012), suitable metrics need to follow some logical rules if they are to be valid for use in transportation planning. Weibull (1976) introduced some basic logical rules for judging the suitability of a proposed metric:

1. The order in which the activities are listed should not affect the value of the measure.
2. The value of the accessibility index should not increase with increasing distance, travel time or travel cost, and should not decrease with increasing attraction.
3. A single activity with infinite attraction situated at zero distance is better than a pair or activities with finite attractions.
4. Activities with zero attraction should not contribute to the accessibility value.
5. The attraction of any activity should not be influenced by surrounding activities.
6. The attraction of any activity is a continuous and increasing function of the size of that activity.

Note that Weibull's rules may exclude the use of generalised cost *per se* as an accessibility metric, as an increased value of travel cost implies reduced accessibility. However, it is still possible to use this metric for comparing accessibility and remoteness, where remoteness is seen as the opposite (or "inverse") of accessibility. More remote locations will have higher levels of generalised costs in accessing services and facilities.

The measure of remoteness, as the inverse of accessibility, may also be used in considerations of network vulnerability. In this case network degradation leads to increased difficulty of access, and thus increases the remoteness of a location in a region. Quantitative assessment of the changes in accessibility or remoteness may then be used to assess the impacts of network failure or degradation at different points in the networks, which can then lead to the identification of critical nodes, links or route segments.

Node-based vulnerability

The D'Este-Taylor definition of vulnerability (see above) considers the vulnerability of a set of nodes in the network, where the set represents facility locations or settlements, and measures vulnerability in terms of changes to accessibility levels dependent on the state of the network. It has been used for studies at the strategic network level (e.g. Taylor, Sekhar and D'Este, 2006; Kurauchi et al., 2009). At this level the node-based representation of cities, towns and settlements is quite reasonable. Similarly, in urban areas where conventional travel demand models are used which represent zones in the area on the basis of zone centroids, the node-based approach is also adequate, at least for strategic planning purposes.

In regional areas, especially those that are sparsely settled, the representation of the region solely in terms of a network of nodes and links may become unrealistic. It may not be feasible to fully represent the population of the region in terms of assumed clusters at network nodes. Location is then a more realistic identifier, and implies the need for a continuum approach to vulnerability analysis. Use of an accessibility-based approach then requires a new definition of vulnerability, couched in terms of locality rather than network structure. An appropriate locality-based definition of network vulnerability is then that given by Taylor and Susilawati (2012):

- A locality in a region served by a transport network is vulnerable if loss (or substantial degradation) of a small number of network links significantly diminishes the accessibility of the locality, as measured by a standard index of remoteness (or accessibility).
- A network link is critical if loss (or substantial degradation) of that link significantly diminishes the accessibility of the region or of particular locations in it, as measured by a standard index of remoteness (or accessibility).

Vulnerability scan

The basic process of a network vulnerability scan for a network is as follows:

1. Compute the accessibility indices for the defined objects in the original network.
2. Compute probabilities of use of different links or route sections (link sequences) in the network, using a multipath traffic assignment procedure.
3. Identify candidate critical links/route sections, as being those for which there are "reasonable" finite probabilities of use.
4. Fail or degrade these candidate links/route sections and determine the new accessibility indices for the defined objects in the degraded network.
5. Determine the resulting changes in accessibility values and identify the most critical links or route sections.

Note that the method may also be applied to scans of network nodes as well as links, by examining the effects of node failure instead of link failure. A node failure will remove or degrade all of the links connected to that node.

Examples of the application of accessibility-based vulnerability analysis in real world transport networks may be found in Sohn (2006); Taylor, Sekhar and D'Este (2006); Chen et al. (2007); Kurauchi et al. (2009); and Taylor and Susilawati (2012). The study by Sohn is of particular interest because it relates a method for accessibility-based vulnerability analysis to flood risk in a region.

Serviceability methods

Serviceability methods focus on the differences in operating conditions on intact and degraded networks. A starting point for considering these methods is the Network Robustness Index (N_R) proposed by Scott et al. (2006). This index compares the total cost of travel in a degraded network to that in the full network, where the degradation is the loss of a link and the travel demand on the network is inelastic. The effect of the loss of the link is thus the rerouting of traffic which would use the link under normal conditions. This rerouting will involve extra travel distance and travel time for the rerouted trips, as well as additional congestion on the other parts of the network now used by the rerouted trips. While the index is formulated in terms of a generalised cost of travel, it is common for this cost to be represented by travel time; thus N_R measures the change in vehicle-hours of travel in the degraded network. Critical links in the network are determined by finding those links which generate the largest values of N_R when closed.

The robustness index is an absolute global measure of the effect of a link closure. As such it provides useful information about the importance of different links in a given network, but it cannot be used to indicate the distribution of effects across different parts of a network (and the region it serves). Nor can it be used for comparative studies between networks serving different regions. Further, the index requires knowledge of the traffic volumes on all links in the network. While such information is available from traffic assignment models, it may not be available for observed volumes.

Researchers at the Royal Institute of Technology, Stockholm have developed a method for network vulnerability analysis which resolves these issues. This is the importance-exposure method (Jenelius, Petersen and Mattsson, 2006; Jenelius and Mattson, 2012). The method is based on the operation assessment of risk – as the product of the probability of network failure and the consequence of the failure. The method is concerned with the potential consequences of network failure on sub regions within a study area, and by the choice of suitable weightings may be used in terms of either "equal opportunities" (where all sub-regions are considered of equal importance) or "social efficiency" (where the sub-regions with larger populations receive more weight). "Exposure" considers the consequences of network failure at a given location. "Importance" considers the impact of that failure on other parts of the study region. Network degradation is allowed to occur on a link or a group of links, on the basis that an extreme event such as flood or blizzard may well affect several components in the network, not just a single link.

The importance and exposure indices may then be defined as follows. Network closure will result in either finite increases in travel cost (possibly zero) for some demand nodes, or unsatisfied demand for other demand nodes. A link which causes finite increases in travel cost when closed is termed a non-cut link. Separate calculations are needed for the non-cut and cut links. Importance and exposure of a link may be calculated either for a single demand node or a group of demand nodes.

Jenelius et al. (2006) applied their method to the regional road network of northern Sweden. More recently, Jenelius and Mattsson (2012) demonstrated how the method can be applied to study the effects of extreme weather events. Snelder et al (2012) extended the use of robustness indicators by developing a consistent framework for robustness to include an evaluation method, which they applied to the main road and motorway network of the Randstad region of the Netherlands. Their method is designed for evaluating the robustness of a road network against short-term variations in supply (e.g. incidents) contributes to the problem of designing robust road networks.

Nagae, Fujihara and Asakura (2012) described a practical method for robustness analysis in large scale networks. They focused on the network design problem for anti-seismic reinforcement (ASR) in a network subject to multiple earthquake risks, using modelled damage patterns on the road network and occurrence probabilities on the basis of recent advances in structural and earthquake engineering. The method was applied to a test scenario of the Kobe region in Japan. The method can be extended to cover extreme weather events such as floods and typhoons given suitable models of the likely extent of damage from such events in a study region.

Developing adaptation responses

In developing adaptation strategies it is critical to understand what the fundamental objective of adaptation is not only for transportation infrastructure and systems, but for the population as a whole. The concept of resilience has been growing in momentum as the desired overall outcome for climate change adaptation of human systems. Resilience is a concept borrowed from ecological systems, and has been defined in the context of urban systems as the capacity to accommodate, or successfully adapt to external threats such as the impacts of enhanced climate change (Hamin and Gurran, 2009). Adaptation strategies are one of the tools required to reduce the vulnerability of urban systems to external threats, thereby limiting the impacts of climate change. For land-based transportation systems, vulnerability must consider the susceptibility of the network to disruptions or degradation that will significantly reduce the efficiency or capability of the operation of the transport system, and the impacts this degradation could have (Sohn, 2006; Taylor, 2008; Freeman et al., 2009).

The implications of climate change for transportation systems discussed in this section are provided in the general Australian context. The actual impacts of climate change are likely to have considerable variation on a regional and local scale. Adaptation measures will have to take this spatial variation into account with localised approaches. This however requires an understanding of localised impacts which in turn requires a framework for risk assessment of land-based transportation infrastructure under climate change. Decision support tools are needed that allow planners and policy makers to assess the threats to infrastructure, the consequences of network degradation and failure at various locations and under different circumstances, and what to do about these (D'Este and Taylor, 2003). Vulnerability assessments are proposed to provide the information necessary to make practical decisions for adapting transport infrastructure to climate change at the appropriate spatial scale. The origin of vulnerability assessments lies in impact assessments and hazard research, and has been applied to map potential climate change impacts and to develop strategies to facilitate adaptation (Fussel and Klein, 2006; Naess et al., 2006). Assessment and prioritisation of adaptation strategies should be conducted considering both the costs and benefits of the economic investment required, with respect to the consequences arising from accessibility restrictions imposed by loss of transport links.

As discussed in the subsection above on liability and insurance, it is the ultimate owner of any piece of infrastructure who must ensure that it is designed to operate effectively for its design life, since they will bear the primary liability in the event of failure (CSIRO, 2006). Responsibility for transport infrastructure in Australia is decentralised and shared between the public and private sectors. The control and expertise required for making decisions regarding climate change adaptation measures for land-based transportation infrastructure are therefore dispersed among multiple levels of government, various authorities and interest groups. These factors raise governance issues with respect to the development of adaptation strategies. Governance is the term used here to refer to the political and legal structures and mechanisms used to manage and co-ordinate transport systems, how they interrelate, how resources are allocated and outcomes are achieved. For example, the governance structures that exist in Australia with implications for transport infrastructure can be summarised as (Commonwealth of Australia 2010ab):

- The Australian Federal Government has stewardship of the national economy and broad interests. As climate change will impact virtually every sector of the economy and society, the federal government must perform a leadership role in adapting Australia to the climate change impacts with direct implications for the economy and Australia's security. With respect to transportation systems, the federal government has specific interests in major land transport networks in relation to their contribution to the productivity of the nation. Input required will be a combination of direct actions, including the management of federal transportation assets, and indirect efforts through the co-ordination of national reform effort. State, territory and local governments deliver more direct services and manage more assets than the federal government, and as such will have to play a bigger role in direct adaptation actions.

- State and territory Governments are responsible for the majority of legislation related to climate change adaptation measures for land-based transportation infrastructure. Metropolitan land use planning, the importance of which is discussed in the previous subsections on planning and liability and insurance, and urban roads and transport have largely been the responsibility of state and territory governments. States and territories fund infrastructure mainly through transfers from the federal government but also from state taxes such as stamp duty.
- Local governments will be key actors in adapting to the local impacts of climate change and engaging in ground level works. Local governments generally have planning authority over land use zoning. Funds for local government to provide infrastructure are sourced from local land rates, and through levies and grants from the other two higher levels of government.

In September 2009 a workshop was conducted in the US, bringing together transportation industry stakeholders from the states of California, Florida, Maryland, Missouri and Washington to discuss climate change adaptation and mitigation from a transportation perspective (AASHTO, 2009). Discussions at the workshop revealed that regardless of jurisdiction, all transportation stakeholders were experiencing the same barriers to climate change adaptation and mitigation which were summarised as (AASHTO, 2009):

- general lack of knowledge on the need to adapt infrastructure for climate change impacts and which adaptation methods should be applied
- governance and communication barriers that prevented co-operation between stakeholders and were in some cases causing agencies to work at cross purposes
- limited funding for planning and implementing adaptation measures.

The generic nature of these barriers and the comparative nature in the governance, urban form and social structures between the United States and Australia suggest that these barriers are also likely to be present in the adaptation of Australian transport infrastructure to climate change (Taylor and Philp, 2010) – and possibly in other contexts as well. The American Association of State Highway and Transportation Officials (AASHTO) workshop participants determined the following set of general approaches that were required to facilitate adapting transportation for climate change (AASHTO, 2009):

- Educate the transportation community about the importance of addressing climate change.
- Top level leadership is needed to provide clarity in policy direction.
- Climate change focussed partnerships should be developed across all governance levels and include private industry.
- Increased assistance and guidance is required to grow institutional capacity to deal with climate change.
- Synergies should be identified among goals and projects being undertaken across all governance levels and private industry.

- Develop new funding strategies.

These approaches provide insight into the needs of the transportation planning community in facilitating adaptation of land-based transportation systems and infrastructure. Each level of government has different responsibilities and therefore will play different roles in adapting transport infrastructure to the impacts of climate change and in providing resilient in the face of extreme weather events. Preparation to deal with climate change impacts will require a whole of government approach to adaptation planning, engaging all levels from federal to local according to the resources and capacity available and to empower private industry and individuals to facilitate the adaptation process.

Figure 3.4. **Structure of the FHWA's conceptual Risk Assessment Model**

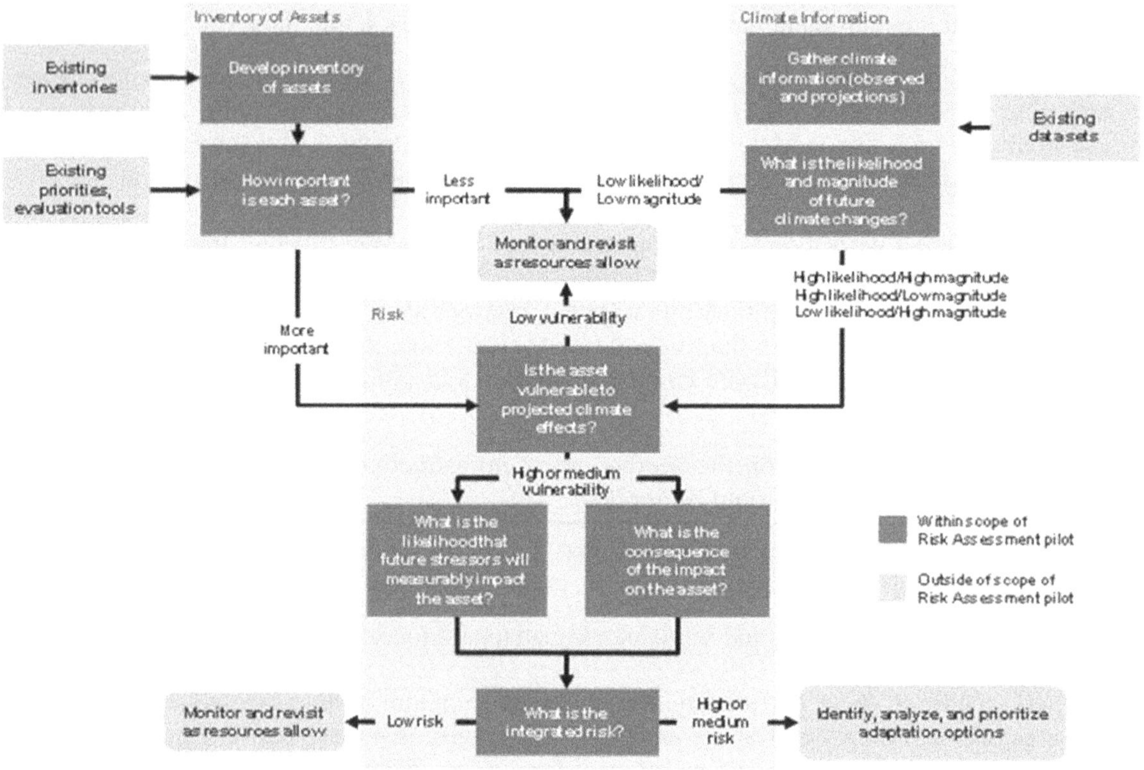

Note: FHWA = US Federal Highways Administration
Source: FHWA, 2010.

Adaptation planning

Two recent examples of planning for the inclusion of climate change and extreme weather impacts may be used to indicate potentially useful planning strategies for transportation systems.

FHWA conceptual model for assessing vulnerability and risk of climate change

The US Federal Highways Administration (FHWA, 2010) recently commissioned a small number of US State Departments of Transportation (DOT) to pilot test a conceptual Risk Assessment Model (RAM). The FHWA intends to use the results of the pilots to develop a final version of the model for all transportation agencies.

The goal of the Risk Assessment Model is to help transportation decision makers (particularly transportation planners, asset managers, and system operators) identify which assets are most exposed to the threats from climate change and/or are associated with the most serious potential consequences of those climate change threats. The conceptual model consists of three primary components, as shown in Figure 3.4:

1. Develop inventory of assets.
2. Gather climate information.
3. Assess the risk to assets and the transportation system as a whole from projected climate change.

The following are the components of the US FHWA Risk Assessment Model.

Develop inventory of assets

The transportation agency first compiles an inventory of all assets they wish to evaluate. Example asset categories are provided below, although any given agency would select asset categories that correspond to their planning priorities. When compiling this inventory, the agency should also gather any information that may help to later evaluate how resilient the asset is to climate stressors, and how costly damage to the asset could be. Example information types are provided in Table 3.2.

Table 3.2. **Indicative asset inventory and information types**

Example asset categories	Example information types
• Bridges and tunnels • Key road segments (and evacuation routes) • Rail (passenger and freight) • Transit system assets • Port and airport assets • Signals and traffic control centres • Back-up power, communication, fuelling, and other emergency operations systems • Intelligent Transportation Systems (ITS), signs • Pipelines • Wetlands • Floodplains • Vegetative Cover	• Age of asset • Geographic location • Elevation • Current/historical performance and condition • Level of use (traffic counts, forecasted demand) • Replacement cost • Repair/maintenance schedule and costs • Structural design • Materials used • Design lifetime and stage of life • LIDAR (Light Detection And Ranging) remote sensing data • Federal Emergency Management (FEMA) maps • Vegetation survey

Importance of each asset

The transportation agency initially screens the assets located in its jurisdiction based on the relative importance of each asset. Using existing priorities and metrics (such as traffic flow, emergency management, movement of goods), the agency should consider which assets are most important for meeting those priorities.

Many transportation agencies have existing evaluation tools or guidelines they use to prioritise assets for maintenance or repair. For example, after a snowstorm, how are roads prioritised for snow removal? Other criteria used to prioritise assets could include the level of usage (annual average daily traffic), class (local roads versus arterials), ownership (a road is privately owned, and not under the agency's jurisdiction), the importance of an asset within the larger transportation network (including potential for adverse network effects), its value in emergency situations (e.g. for evacuation), and/or redundancy. The loss of a particular asset may have ripple effects through the network that make an asset important to include in the Risk Assessment Model.

Gather climate information

As an agency develops its asset inventory, it will also gather local- or regional-level information on past changes and projections of future climate. The agency can use this information to assess impact. FHWA expects to be able to assist agencies in using this information to translate projected climate changes into tangible climate-related impacts on the transportation system. Therefore each agency is advised to revisit this step as new information becomes available.

Historical climate and weather information will provide clues as to how assets may withstand future climate stressors. Projected climate information, is important for estimating future climate conditions to plan for. Both of these types of information will be used later in this risk assessment with the caveat that both are imperfect predictors of future asset-level climate impacts.

What is the likelihood[2] and magnitude of future climate changes?

Each climate dataset has associated uncertainties.[3] Uncertainties are generally smaller with observational data than with projections of future climate conditions. The range of uncertainty associated with future projections has been characterised for major US regions in the Climate Change Effects Report developed by FHWA.[4]

A screening analysis should be conducted at this stage to set aside potential climate change effects that are both relatively uncertain (e.g., the sign of the change is unknown) and small in magnitude. These potential effects may be revisited at a later time. Potential changes that should not be screened out at this stage are those that are relatively uncertain but possibly large (e.g. changes in hurricane characteristics), and those that are relatively certain but small in magnitude (e.g. regional temperature changes). Judgments about the significance of the magnitude will be subjective since a change in one climate variable may be significant to one region or transportation mode, but insignificant to another. FHWA will work with the agencies to provide guidance on how to take uncertainty and magnitude into account.

Assessing risk

Risk is the potential for an unwanted outcome resulting from an event-in this case, a climate stressor. It is determined by the product of the likelihood of the impact and the consequence of the impact.[5] The likelihood of an impact is, in part, a function of the likelihood of the climate stressors. It is also a function of the vulnerability of the transportation element to climate change. Vulnerability also affects the magnitude of the impact.

In this phase, agencies will: (1) screen assets that are less vulnerable to projected climate effects; (2) assess the likelihood of a particular impact resulting from a defined set of stressors, (3) assess the consequence of the impact, not just in terms of what it does to a particular asset, but in terms of how it affects the surrounding community and beyond, and (4) assess the integrated risk of the consequence and likelihood.

Assess vulnerability using historical weather information

By understanding how weather events had previously affected an asset, a transportation agency will be better able to understand how weather events in the future may affect that asset or similar assets. Furthermore, historical experience may provide information on the significance of the impact to the transportation system if a certain asset is damaged or destroyed. To address this question, the agency should consider the historical performance of assets during specific weather events. For example, it could consider:

- the repair costs or retrofits caused by past weather events
- budgets and spending for services that respond to weather events (e.g. snow ploughing)
- effects of past weather events on services provided by an asset (e.g. changes in VMT(VKT), the value of the goods transported
- the role of the asset in emergency response and evacuations required in past weather events.

By comparing historical weather events with historical maintenance and repair needs, an agency can estimate how well specific assets withstand certain climate stressors. In doing so, it may be able to identify physical or environmental characteristics that make a structure more or less vulnerable to a given climate stressor. If a specific climate stressor does not appear to have a significant effect on a given asset, agencies may screen that climate stressor-asset combination from the assessment, record it, and revisit it as resources allow. Crucially, agencies should assess the range of uncertainties associated with each climate stressor and their potential combination and frequency going forward. The past historic meteorological record may be an imperfect basis on which to assess mid- and long-range climate impacts.

Each agency should identify information sources that could be consulted or compiled to evaluate the effects of current climate stressors on assets, and will assist agencies in identifying climate stressors that are already taken into account in the design, operation, and maintenance of existing assets.

Assess whether future climate change introduces additional climate vulnerability

At this point, the agency should have a good sense of how well assets can withstand specific climate stressors, many of which may be present (and perhaps be more/less frequent) in the future. However, projected climate scenarios may include stressors to which assets are currently not exposed. For example, climate projections may indicate that an asset will likely be exposed to extreme temperatures not previously experienced. The projected extreme temperatures may exceed certain thresholds at which the asset material is compromised. Or, some assets may have been exposed to temporary flooding, but projected climate information may indicate longer-term inundation, which can have very different impacts on an asset. Finally, agencies must consider the cumulative impacts of more frequent climate stressors; a particular asset may be able to withstand the first and second flood (for example) in a given year, but not the third flood.

Agencies will need to apply climate projections to evaluate the likelihood of future impacts, including cumulative effects from changes in several climate stressors. To the extent that information is available, impacts will be split into high- and low-likelihood groupings. Transportation agencies will have the flexibility to define what a "severe" climate effect means for them, and effects that are determined to be less severe can be recorded and revisited as resources allow. Projected changes in climate that are so uncertain that it is not possible to determine whether future stressors will measurably impact the asset should be accounted for in planning responses that favour flexible approaches and minimise regrets in light of potentially large and uncertain impacts.

What is the integrated risk of climate change to the asset?

For assets deemed "vulnerable", the integrated risk assessment for an asset should jointly consider the likelihood that the asset will experience a particular impact, and the consequence of that impact on the surrounding community or region (from a health/safety, economic, environmental, cultural, or other point of view). Assets that have a low likelihood of being impacted by future climate and a low consequence of that impact occurring will be screened, recorded, and revisited as resources allow. The remaining assets, grouped according to high/low likelihood and high/low consequence of impact, is the outcome of the Risk Assessment Model. As a result of this analysis, the agency will have a prioritised list of assets at risk from future climate change impacts, developed according to their own criteria. The integrated risk is often represented by a two-dimensional matrix that classifies risks into three categories (low, moderate, high) based on the combined effects of their likelihood and consequence. An example matrix from the 2006 FHWA document Risk Assessment and Allocation for Highway Construction Management is provided in Figure 3.5.

Figure 3.5. **Classification of risks to an asset according to categories of likelihood and consequence**

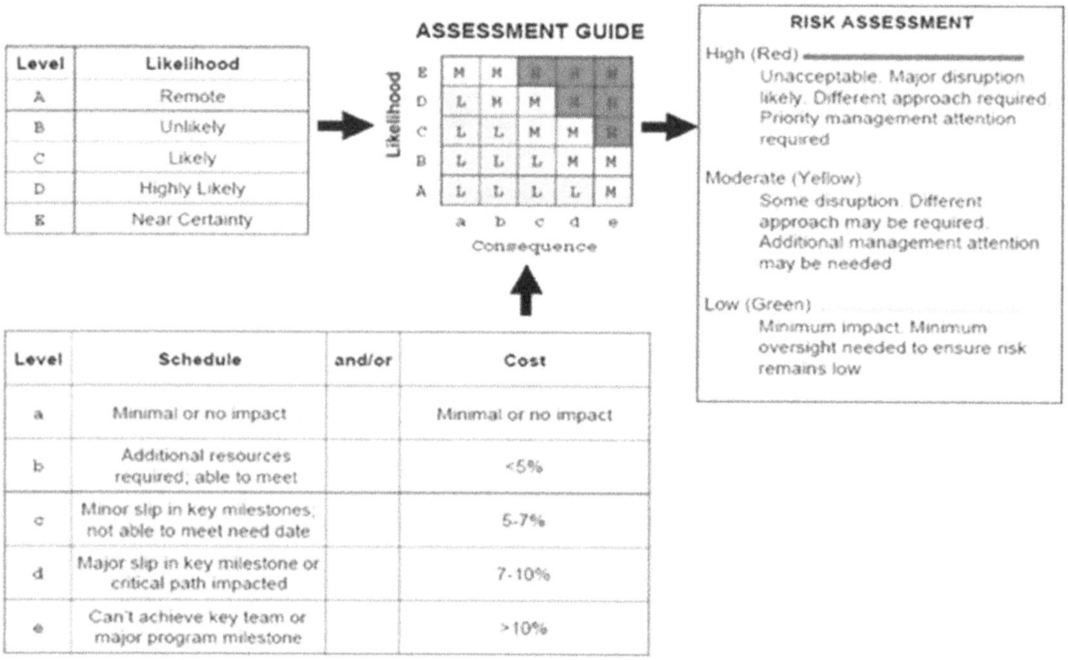

Source: FHWA, 2010.

A decision support system for evacuation planning

As discussed previously, the uncertainty of climate change acts as one of the barriers to long term adaptation. Decision support systems are designed to assist in planning decisions where future conditions are uncertain or can change rapidly. As such decision support systems can prove useful in adaptation planning, as shown in the following discussion with respect to evacuation planning.

A specification for a decision support system for emergency management and evacuation planning can be written as follows. For a simple macroscopic model that can provide planning guidance for the evacuation of people from threatened areas to safe designated shelters outside or inside the threatened area, the following model features are required (Taylor and Freeman, 2010):

- The simplicity of the model should not be achieved at the expense of reliable results and appropriate detail.
- The model should be dynamic in updating both the state of the emergency and the levels of road access, traffic conditions, volumes, travel times and (if appropriate) queuing.
- The model needs to include and provide realistic measures of intersection, link and network capacities. This must include specific realisation of the capacity and characteristics of traffic flow on two-way two-lane roads with restricted sight distances.
- The model requires the capability to evaluate the impacts of future land use plans and population distribution and intensity on evacuation times and rates.
- The model must include good representation of the behaviour of individuals.
- The major application of the model is for strategic planning, based on scenario studies for different natural disasters (including intensity and location) under a range of environmental and meteorological conditions.
- The model's outputs will be used to inform and assist the strategic planning processes in a locality, in conjunction with local knowledge and available professional expertise.
- The model should be developed in a dynamic geographic information system (GIS) software platform, including and integrating accurate road network, terrain and topography, land use and population, and vegetation, environmental and meteorological databases.

The vital position of dynamic GIS as the underlying software platform support for the model has already been identified (e.g. Ahola et al., 2007; Taylor and Freeman, 2010). Given the existence of comprehensive and accurate data on physical characteristics (e.g. terrain, topography, vegetation and environment), demographics and land use, infrastructure and facilities (e.g. road networks, water supply and electricity distribution), the GIS platform provides the means to integrate the databases and to host the different computational models. In addition, the road network model attached to the GIS is used to determine both shortest paths from inhabited zones to shelters and also "second-best" paths. Similar path calculations would be made for use by emergency services when seeking to reach any specified locations. Path determination is done initially for the normal, full and intact network as the base case.

Disaster scenarios may then be simulated for different scenarios, using (in the case of bushfires) a model such as Phoenix (Tolhurst et al., 2008), to be run with different meteorological conditions and fire ignition points. The paths and impacts of the simulated fires can then be used to determine the likely consequences for the road network. For instance, Sohn (2006) used a similar approach to establish vulnerable links in a regional road network subject to flooding. In the case of bushfire modelling, the analysis would be undertaken from two perspectives. First would be the identification of likely weak spots in the road network, being links and road sections most likely to be affected (i.e. degraded or closed) by fires. Second would be the identification of resilient links and road sections, being those parts of the network least likely to be affected by fires. That is, both network vulnerability and network resilience are important considerations. Outputs from the model would include qualified advice about most reliable evacuation routes – and access routes for emergency services. Qualification of the advice is necessary because of the significant stochastic variations in circumstances inherent in the natural disaster scenarios (e.g. Yuan et al., 2006; Murray-Tuite, 2007).

A similar analysis approach could be adopted for flood scenarios. The NSW SES (Opper et al., 2010) has developed a conceptual model for flood evacuation assessment and planning. The estimation of evacuation timing and duration using this model would benefit greatly from a better understanding of the influence of human behaviour and of realistic road traffic capacity under flood conditions. Furthermore, traffic movements on rural road networks need to be studied and modelled with care, because of the unique nature of traffic flows on such roads.

The identification of vulnerable links in a network can be undertaken using the recently developed methods for network vulnerability analysis and the determination of critical locations, as described in Jenelius et al. (2006), Taylor (2008) and Taylor and Susilawati (2012). Modifications to the approach can be made to identify the most resilient links as well as the most vulnerable ones. It is likely that a combination of the criticality and importance metrics introduced by Jenelius et al. (2006) and the area-accessibility-based vulnerability analysis method described by Taylor and Susilawati (2012) – which is firmly embedded in a GIS framework – should produce a valid and practical assessment methodology for network assessment.

Figure 3.6 outlines a decision support system designed to assist in planning for emergency management and evacuations in the face of a given hazard or natural disaster, based on the availability of models for predicting the intensity and trajectory of a given disaster[6] (e.g. the Phoenix model for wild fires, Tolhurst et al., 2008).

Figure 3.6. **Proposed decision support system for transport aspects of emergency management and evacuation planning**

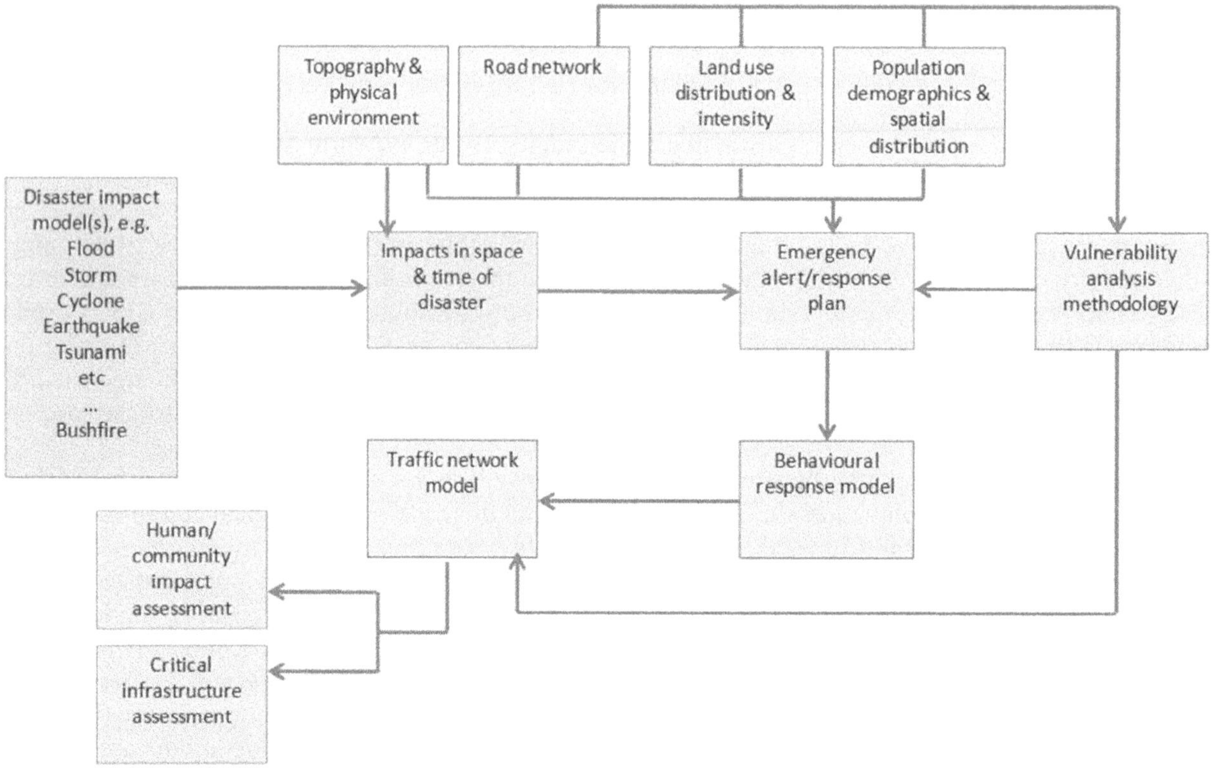

Source: Taylor and Philp, 2010.

References

AASHTO (American Association of State Highway and Transportation Officials) (2009), "Integrated state and local government policy approaches to transportation and climate change: A summary of the executive peer exchange", Center for Clean Air Policy, Washington D.C.

Ahola, T., K. Virrantaus, J. Krisp and G. Hunter (2007), "A Spatio-temporal Population Model to Support Risk Assessment and Damage Analysis for Decision-making", *International Journal of Geographical Information Science*, Vol. 21, pp. 935-953.

Asakura, Y. (1999), "Evaluation of Network Reliability Using Stochastic User Equilibrium". *Journal of Advanced Transportation*, Vol. 33/2, pp. 147-158.

Attorney-General's Department (2003), Trusted information sharing network for critical infrastructure protection (10 March 2003) Attorney-General's Department, Canberra.

Auld, H., D. MacIver and J. Klaassen (2006), "Adaptation options for infrastructure under changing climate conditions", Environment Canada, Ottawa.

Austroads (2009a), "Guide to Asset Management Part 1: Introduction to asset management". Publication no AGAM01/09, Austroads, Sydney.

Austroads (2009b), "Guide to Asset Management Part 1: Asset strategies". Publication no AGAM03/09, Austroads, Sydney.

Bates, J, J. Polak, P. Jones and A. Cook (2001), "The Valuation of Reliability for Personal Travel". *Transportation Research*, Vol. 37, pp. 191-229.

Bell, M.G.H. and C. Cassir (eds.) (2000), *Reliability of Transport Networks*. Research Studies Press, Baldock, Herts.

Bell, M.G.H and Y. Iida (1997), Transportation Network Analysis. John Wiley and Sons, Chichester.

Berdica, K. (2002), "An Introduction to Road Vulnerability: What has been done, is done and should be done". *Transport Policy*, Vol. 9, pp. 117-127.

Berdica, K. and L.G. Mattsson (2007), "Vulnerability: A model-based case study of the road network in Stockholm", in Murray, A.T. and T.H. Grubesic (eds), *Critical Infrastructure: Reliability and Vulnerability*. Springer, New York, pp.81-106.

Bonsall, P.W. (2000), "Travellers' response to uncertainty", in Bell, M.G.H and C. Cassir (eds.) *Reliability of Transport Networks*. Research Studies Press, Baldock, Herts, pp.1-10.

Brown, D, S. Moin and M. Nicholson (1997), "A Comparison of Flooding in Michigan and Ontario: Soft data to support soft water management approaches". *Canadian Water Resources Journal*, Vol. 22/2, pp. 125-139.

BTRE (2002), "Benefits of flood mitigation in Australia". Report 106, Bureau of Transport and Regional Economics, Canberra.

Chen, A., H. Yang, H.K. Lo and W.H Tang (1999), "A capacity related reliability for transportation networks". *Journal of Advanced Transportation*, Vol. 33/2, pp. 183-200.

Chen, A, S. Kongsomsaksakul, Z. Zhou, M. Lee and W. Recker (2007), "Assessing network vulnerability of degradable transportation systems: An accessibility based approach", in Allsop, R.E., M.G.H. Bell and B. Heydecker (eds.) *Transportation and Traffic Theory 2007*. Elsevier, Oxford, pp. 237–262.

Commonwealth of Australia (2010a), "Adapting to climate change in Australia – an Australian Government position paper". Department of Climate Change, Canberra.

Commonwealth of Australia (2010b), "State of Australian cities", Department of Infrastructure, Transport and the Regions, Canberra.

CSIRO (2006), "Infrastructure and climate change risk assessment for Victoria". Report to Victorian Government, CSIRO Division of Atmospheric Physics, Melbourne.

D'Este, G.M. and M.A.P. Taylor (2003), "Network vulnerability: An approach to reliability analysis at the level of national strategic transport networks", in Iida, Y. and M.G.H. Bell (eds.) *The Network Reliability of Transport*. Pergamon-Elsevier, Oxford, pp.23-44.

D'Este, G.M. and M.A.P. Taylor (2001), "Modelling Network Vulnerability at the Level of the National Strategic Transport Network". *Journal of the Eastern Asia Society for Transportation Studies*, Vol. 4/2, pp. 1-14.

Edwards, J. (1999), "The Temporal Distribution of Road Accidents in Adverse Weather". *Journal of Applied Meteorology*, Vol. 6, pp. 59-68.

Evans, C., D. Tsolakis and C. Naude (2009), "Framework to address climate change impacts on road infrastructure assets and operations". Papers of the 32nd Australasian Transport Research Forum, Auckland, www.patrec.org/atrf.aspx

Evans, A. (1994), "Evaluating public transport and road safety measures". *Accident Analysis and Prevention*, Vol. 26, pp. 411-428.

FHWA (2010), "Assessing vulnerability and risk of climate change effects on transportation infrastructure: pilot of the conceptual model". Federal Highways Administration, Washington D.C. www.fhwa.dot.gov/environment/climate_change/adaptation/ongoing_and_current_research/vulnerability_assessment_pilots/conceptual_model62410.pdf

FHWA (2006), "Travel time reliability: making it there on time, all the time". Federal Highway Administration, US Department of Transportation, Washington D.C. http://ops.fhwa.dot.gov/publications/tt_reliability/TTR_Report.htm

Freeman, S., M.A.P. Taylor and N.M. Holyoak (2009), "Vulnerability analysis of road networks". Papers of the 32nd Australasian Transport Research Forum, Auckland, www.patrec.org/atrf.aspx

Fu, H. and C.G. Wilmot (2004), "Sequential Logit Dynamic Travel Demand Model for Hurricane Evacuation. *Transportation Research Record*, Vol. 1882, pp.19-26.

Fussel, H. and R. Klein (2006), "Climate Change Vulnerability Assessments: An evolution of conceptual thinking". *Climatic Change*, Vol. 75, pp. 301-329.

Garnaut, R. (2008), *The Garnaut Climate Change Review*. Cambridge University Press, Melbourne.

Herman, R. and T. Lam (1974) "Trip time characteristics of journeys to and from work", in Buckley, D.J. (ed) *Transportation and Traffic Theory*. A.H. and A.W. Reed, Sydney, pp.57-85.

Hamin, E. and N. Gurran (2009), "Urban form and climate change: balancing adaptation and migration in the US and Australia", *Habitat International*, Vol. 33, pp. 445-65.

Iida, Y. (1999), "Basic Concepts and Future Directions of Road Network Reliability Analysis". *Journal of Advanced Transportation*, Vol. 33/2, pp. 125-134.

Iida, Y. and M.G.H. Bell (eds.) (2003), *The Network Reliability of Transport*. Pergamon-Elsevier, Oxford.

ITF (2010), *Improving Reliability on Surface Transport Networks*, OECD Publishing, Paris. DOI: http://dx.doi.org/10.1787/9789282102428-en

Jenelius, E. and L.G. Mattsson (2012), "Road Network Vulnerability Analysis of Area-covering Disruptions: A grid-based approach with case study". *Transportation Research A*, Vol. 46/5, pp. 746-760.

Jenelius, E., T. Petersen and L.G. Mattsson. (2006), "Importance and Exposure in Road Network Vulnerability Analysis". *Transportation Research A*, Vol. 40, pp. 537-560.

Jaroszweski, D, L. Chapman and J. Petts (2010), "Assessing the Potential Impact of Climate Change on Transportation: The need for an interdisciplinary approach". *Journal of Transport Geography*, Vol. 18, pp. 331-335.

Koetse, M. and P. Rietveld (2009), "The Impact of Climate Change and Weather on Transport: An Overview of Emperical Findings". *Transportation Research: Part D*, Vol. 14. pp. 205-221.

Keay, K. and I. Simmonds (2005), "The Association of Rainfall and Other Weather Variables with Road Traffic Volume in Melbourne, Australia". *Accident Analysis and Prevention*, Vol. 37, pp. 109-124.

Kurauchi, F, N. Uno, A. Sumalee and Y. Seto (2009), "Network evaluation based on connectivity vulnerability", in Lam, W.H.K., S.C. Wong and H.K. Lo (eds.) *Transportation and Traffic Theory 2009*, Springer, New York, pp.637-649.

Lam, W.H.K. (ed) (1999), "Special Issue on Transport Network Reliability". *Journal of Advanced Transportation*, Vol. 33/2.

Lam, W.H.K. and G. Xu (2000), "Calibration of traffic flow simulator for network reliability assessment", in Bell, M.G.H. and C. Cassir (eds.), Re*liability of Transport Networks*. Research Studies Press, Baldock, Herts, pp.139-157.

Lee, C.E. (1946), "New Works for Wartime Traffic". *The Railway Magazine*, Vol. 92, pp. 177-83.

Lindell, M.K. and C.S. Prater (2007), "Critical Behavioral Assumptions in Evacuation Time Estimate Analysis for Private Vehicles: Examples from hurricane research and planning". *ASCE Journal of Urban Planning and Development*, Vol. 133, pp. 18-29.

Litman, T. (2006), "Lessons from Katrina and Rita: what major disasters can teach transportation planners". Victoria Transport Policy Institute, Victoria, www.vtpi.com

Middlemann, M. (ed.) (2007), "Natural hazards in Australia: Identifying risk analysis requirement", *Geoscience Australia*, Canberra.

MunichRe (2009), "Natural catastrophes 2008: Analyses, assessments, positions". Australasia/Oceania Volume, MunichRe, Munich.

Murray, A.T. and T.H. Grubesic (eds.) (2007), *Critical Infrastructure: Reliability and Vulnerability*. Springer, New York, pp. 81-106.

Murray-Tuite, P. (2007), "Perspectives for Network Management in Response to Unplanned Disruptions". *ASCE Journal of Urban Planning and Development*, Vol. 133, pp. 9-17.

Naess, L., I. Norland, W. Lafferty and C. Aall (2006), "Data and Processes Linking Vulnerability Assessment to Adaptation Decision Making on Climate Change in Norway". *Global Environmental Change*, Vol. 16, pp. 221-233.

Nicholson, A.J. and E. Dalziell (2003), "Risk evaluation and management: A road network reliability study", in Iida, Y. and M.G.H. Bell (eds.), *The Network Reliability of Transport*. Pergamon-Elsevier, Oxford, pp. 45-59.

Niemeier, D.A. (1997), "Accessibility: An evaluation using consumer welfare". *Transportation*, Vol. 24, pp. 377-396.

Opper, S., P. Cinque and B. Davies (2010), "Timeline Modelling of Flood Evacuation Operations". *Procedia Engineering*, Vol. 3, pp. 175-187.

Primerano, F. and M.A.P. Taylor (2005), "An accessibility framework for evaluating transport policies", in Levinson, D.M. and K.J. Krizek (eds.), *Access to Destinations*. Elsevier, Oxford, pp.325-346.

Richardson, A.J. and M.A.P. Taylor (1978), "A Study of Travel Time Variability on Commuter Journeys". *High Speed Ground Transportation Journal*, Vol. 12/1, pp. 77-99.

Rowland, B., J. Davey, J. Freeman and D. Wishart (2007), "Road transport sensitivities to weather and climate change in Australia: A review of climate change effects". Papers of the 30th Australasian Transport Research Forum, Melbourne, www.patrec.org/atrf.aspx

Scott, D.M., D.C. Novak, L. Aultman-Hall and F. Guo (2006), "Network Robustness Index: A new method for identifying critical links and evaluating the performance of transportation networks". *Journal of Transport Geography*, Vol. 14, pp. 215-227.

Sohn, J. (2006), "Evaluating the Significance of Highway Network Links Under the Flood Damage: An accessibility approach". *Transportation Research Part A*, Vol. 40, pp.491-506.

Stern, E. and Y. Zehavi (1990), "Road Safety and Hot Weather: A study in applied transport geography". *Transactions of the Institute of British Geographers*, Vol. 15, pp. 102-111.

Snelder, M., H.J. Van Zuylen and L.H. Immers (2012), "A Framework for Robustness Analysis of Road Networks for Short Term Variations in Supply". *Transportation Research Part A*, Vol. 46/5, pp. 828-842.

Taylor, M.A.P. (2008), "Critical Transport Infrastructure in Urban Areas: Impacts of traffic incidents assessed using accessibility based network vulnerability analysis". *Growth and Change*, Vol. 39, pp. 593-616.

Taylor, M.A.P. (2000), "Using network reliability concepts for traffic calming – permeability, approachability and tortuosity – in network design", in Bell, M.G.H. and C. Cassir (eds.), *Reliability of Transport Networks*. Research Studies Press, Baldock, Herts, pp. 217-242.

Taylor, M.A.P. (1999), "Dense Network Traffic Models, Travel Time Reliability and Traffic Management II: Application to reliability". *Journal of Advanced Transportation*, Vol. 33/2, pp. 235-251.

Taylor, M.A.P. (1982), "Travel Time Variability: The case of two public modes". *Transportation Science*, Vol. 16/2, pp. 517-521.

Taylor, M.A.P., S.V.C. Sekhar and G.M. D'Este (2006), "Application of Accessibility Based Methods for Vulnerability Analysis of Strategic Road Networks". *Networks and Spatial Economics*, Vol. 6/3-4, pp. 267-291.

Taylor, M.A.P. and S.K. Freeman (2010), "A Review of Planning and Operational Models Used for Emergency Evacuation Situations in Australia". *Procedia Engineering*, Vol. 3, pp. 3-14.

Taylor, M.A.P. and M. Philp (2010), "Adapting to Climate Change – implications for transport infrastructure, transport systems and travel behaviour". *Road and Transport Research*, Vol. 19/4, pp.66-78.

Taylor, M.A.P. and Susilawati (2012), "Remoteness and Accessibility in the Vulnerability Analysis of Regional Road Networks". *Transportation Research Part A*, Vol. 46/5, pp. 761-771.

Tolhurst, K., B. Shields and D. Chong (2008), "Phoenix: Development and application of a bushfire risk management tool". *Australian Journal of Emergency Management*, Vol. 23, pp. 47-54.

TRB (2008), "Potential impacts of climate change on US transportation". Special Report no 290, Transportation Research Board, Washington D.C.

Unrau, D. and J. Andrey (2006), "Driver Response to Rainfall on Urban Expressways". *Transportation Research Record*, Vol. 1980, pp. 24-30.

USDOT (2002), "The potential impacts of climate change for transportation". DOT Center for Climate Change and Environmental Forecasting, Washington, D.C.

Weibull, J.W. (1976), "Axiomatic Approach to the Measurement of Accessibility". *Regional Science and Urban Economics*, Vol. 6, pp. 357-379.

Wolshon, B. and B. Meehan (2003), "Emergency Evacuation: Ensuring safe and efficient transportation out of endangered areas". *TR News*, Vol. 224, pp. 3-9.

Yang, H, H.K. Lo and W.H. Tang (2000), "Travel time versus capacity reliability of a road network", in Bell, M.G.H. and C. Cassir (eds), *Reliability of Transport Networks*. Research Studies Press, Baldock, Herts, pp. 119-138.

Yuan, F., L. Han, S. Chin and H. Hwang (2006), "Proposed Framework for Simultaneous Optimization of Evacuation Traffic Destination and Route Assignment". *Transportation Research Record*, Vol. 1964, pp. 50-58.

Notes

1 The solid diamond background in Figure 3.1 is a representation of the many interactions and relationships between the key elements which, if shown separately, would appear as an extremely complex diagram.

2 In this chapter, "likelihood" refers to the general probability of occurrence and is used preferentially over the term "probability", because it colloquially denotes a probability range, rather than a single value. As discussed in the climate assessments from the Intergovernmental Panel on Climate Change (IPCC) and the US Global Change Research Program, it is generally not possible to assign a single integer of the percent probability to a particular future climate effect.

3 "Uncertainty" is an expression of the degree to which a value (e.g. the future state of the climate system) is unknown. In general terms, uncertainty can result from lack of information or from disagreement about what is known. (From IPCC, 2007, Glossary of Terms. http://www.ipcc.ch/pdf/glossary/ar4-wg1.pdf). See Chapter 4 for a further discussion of uncertainty.

4 See http://www.fhwa.dot.gov/hep/climate/climate_effects/index.cfm

5 As defined by the US Department of Homeland Security in its 2009 *National Infrastructure Protection Plan*. See www.dhs.gov/xlibrary/assets/NIPP_Plan.pdf, p. 27.

6 Noting that not all of the potential natural disasters are attributable to or influenced by climate change. The decision support system could also be used to consider man-made interventions and disasters, such as terrorist attacks or explosions.

Chapter 4. Managing climate change uncertainty in transport infrastructure design and network planning

Managing uncertainty is not a new aspect of transport policy – considerable climate change uncertainty surrounds future demand projections and the global trends that can impact flows of people and goods. There is also micro-level uncertainty on how specific parts of the transport networks may be affected by disruptions. Addressing these incidents and sources of uncertainty lies at the heart of transport decision making. This chapter looks at strategies including, but not limited to, cost-benefit analysis to address this "deep" uncertainty for transport infrastructure and services whose life-times extend well into the future.

Transport asset managers face a fundamentally uncertain future with respect to infrastructure and network vulnerability to climate change and future extreme weather events. Broad evidence supports the view that man-made emissions of greenhouse gases are changing the climate, yet considerable uncertainty remains over the exact scale, scope and regional impacts of climate change which complicates adaptation efforts. This uncertainty remains irrespective of the source of climate change (anthropogenic or natural) and is sensitive to our understanding of the physical processes that link observed increases in atmospheric greenhouse gas concentrations to changes in climate. Nonetheless, despite this uncertainty, decision-makers must still make investment decisions that maximise public welfare and deliver on public policy objectives. This section explores the nature of uncertainty linked to climate change adaptation efforts and explores principles and tools for decision making under these uncertainties.

Climate change uncertainty in the context of adaptation efforts

Normally, meteorological and climate factors fall into the range of manageable risks that asset managers must contend with. In fact, in many ways, they are one of the principal risks that asset owners must address because they have the potential to significantly, and sometimes suddenly, degrade assets and network performance. For this reason, historic climate and meteorological variables are embedded in both the siting of transport networks and the design specifications of specific assets. This ensures that infrastructure continues to operate under a range of expected meteorological conditions and weather phenomena. Even though the natural variability of extreme weather events may cause significant disruption, if asset owners have undertaken due diligence in both the planning and design phases of infrastructure deployment, these risks are generally well known and are more-or-less contained. This is may no longer be true since under a changing climate regime, both meteorological and climate parameters are changing in uncertain ways leading to difficult-to-predict end-states. Indeed, many infrastructure owners and managers already have to come to grips with the implications of climate change for the performance of their assets and networks. Here, the "embeddedness" of climate variables in transport infrastructure places assets and network service continuity at risk. – both at potentially significant costs.

Part of the difficulty facing asset owners and managers is that the decision-support mechanisms that were used to assess existing infrastructure are less and less adapted to assessing their replacements or, for that matter, understanding forward-going risks (Patt, Hinkel and Swart, 2011;Watkiss et al., 2012). That is because the science behind understanding future climate change impacts is based neither on observational data of future climate nor on experimental approaches but rather on models. While the models used for climate projections are informed by observational data, the models produce representations of future climates that extend well beyond the range of the climate in which the data that informs these representations were gathered (Patt, Hinkel and Swart, 2011). These models, as described in Chapter 1, assemble numerous uncertainties that cannot be reduced through observation. The cascading uncertainties include uncertainty on:

- the volume of greenhouse gases emitted over time
- the sequestration rate for these gases and thus their resultant atmospheric concentration
- the response rate of global temperatures to these evolving atmospheric concentrations
- the impacts these changes in temperature will have on hydro-meteorological phenomena at finer and finer spatial resolution
- how these changes in hydro-meteorological cycles (and sea level rise) will impact ecosystems, the built environment
- how humans will react and/or adapt to these impacts.

For all of these, the larger the range of uncertainty, the smaller the likelihood that the mean of the projected range will be near the actual future value. Thus, in the absence of explicit likelihood information for a particular variable, the range of uncertainty may provide some guidance to approximate likelihood. For some of the uncertainties listed above, the ranges of outcomes can be described in a quantitative manner while, given current knowledge, this may not be possible for many others. Walker et al. (2003) describes a gradient running from deterministic knowledge to indeterminacy (Figure 4.1) that helps frame uncertainty for decision making. In the context of climate change, statistical uncertainty may be associated with the observation of existing climate variables that may include some observational biases, scenario uncertainty may extend to knowledge about policy responses to (uncertain) levels of emissions and their efficacy, and recognised ignorance may describe the current state of knowledge on certain hydro-meteorological feedback cycles and which calls for competing models to provide a range of plausible future outcomes. Various alternate scenarios and analysis pathways may compensate for these three types of uncertainties – but there are some things that fall outside of the range of the deterministic – these are things we do not know we do not know – or complete indeterminacy (Walker et al., 2003). All of these types of uncertainty, and the latter one especially, matter for climate change adaptation policy and will require tools and approaches that help guide decision making despite imperfect knowledge about climate change.

Figure 4.1. **Knowledge-ignorance gradient for uncertainty management**

Source: Walker et al., 2003.

A changing climate poses two fundamental challenges to infrastructure owners. The first is that they must ensure continued asset performance under sometimes significantly modified climate conditions – conditions which may decrease the present value of their networks or increase maintenance and refurbishment costs, or vice-versa. The second challenge is that authorities or private operators must design and build new or replacement assets in the context of these same changing and largely uncertain climate variables. Uncertainty regarding these variables runs the risk of over- or under-specification of infrastructure design standards. Over-specification of design standards results in stranded or non-productive investments whereas under-specification may lead to asset failure or network service degradation. These are important risks for public authorities who are tasked with delivering satisfactory and predictable transport services and for private operators who must realise expected returns for their investors.

Critical to this dual task is the ability for authorities or private entities to assess options, including capital investment options, to deliver transport services in spite of this uncertainty. A number of decision-support tools are available to undertake this appraisal, and the first among these is cost-benefit analysis (CBA). Other traditional transport appraisal techniques include cost-effectiveness analysis and multi-criteria analysis.

Traditional decision support tools

Cost-benefit analysis

Cost-benefit analysis (CBA) is one of the most widely used decision-support tools for guiding transport investments. CBA places a value on relevant costs and benefits to society of considered options and then estimates the net present value of these taking into account the life of the investment and a selected discount rate. It is up to the decision maker to select the time horizon of discounting and required returns on investment. For transport system investments the horizon varies according to the technical life span of the investment. For transport infrastructures, such as roads and railways, the horizon is typically 20-50 years. For some systems, such as traffic control systems which involve information and communication technologies, the life span of which is much shorter, usually not more than 10 years.

Cost-benefit calculus can be used for any investment or activity that marginally changes the behaviour or performance of the system under analysis. In transport infrastructure projects, it is the network that is changed and the aforementioned savings are pursued by the investment capital outlay.

The costs of crashes and environmental items are usually considered externalities, i.e. costs that are not borne within the system (users of the mobility system, infrastructure owners, etc.) but by third parties or society as a whole. Benefits can also be external, but these are difficult to capture and are often excluded from standard analysis. The boundaries of cost-benefit analysis must be decided on beforehand; as the externalities can extend indefinitely they cannot all be considered in practice.

Extreme weather and climate change risks (costs) represent a new type of externality which should be addressed in CBA. No standard procedure exists to do this, although some basic principles have been introduced in analytical format (see e.g. Frankhauser et al., 1999). Routine CBA may not be suited for assessing medium-term or long-lived investments in light of climate change. That is because CBA is an "Agree on Assumptions" approach that first seeks agreement on current and future conditions (e.g. either discretely as in the statistical value of life or through a probability distribution regarding future demand levels), analyses options and picks an optimal outcome. "Agree on Assumption" appraisal works best when stakeholders can agree on the quantification of impacts and how these impacts should be valued over time.

Where the probability of future climate impacts can be robustly assessed and where agreement can be found on both the quantification of non-monetised impacts and discount rates, CBA retains its usefulness. Risk-adjusted discount rates and providing decision makers with explicit assessments of climate-related uncertainties can help improve CBA (ITF, 2014). However, many climate change impacts are subject to deep and cascading uncertainty and cannot be assigned objective or subjective probabilities. Likewise, agreement on other inputs to CBA may be difficult to obtain in light of a changing climate. These shortcomings limit the usefulness of cost-benefit analysis as a stand-alone approach to guide transport investments for long-lived infrastructure in light of climate change.

The EWENT project identified three types of cost categories for CBA in the context of climate change and extreme weather: crash-related costs, time costs, and infrastructure-related costs. The latter comprised physical damages to infrastructure and increased maintenance costs (Nokkala et al., 2012). In the EWENT project framework, only crash-related costs were regarded as externalities, but even this can be debated as most crash-related costs are typically covered either by insurance or by users of the transport system themselves. Hence, in theory, most extreme weather costs should already be internalised, but they in fact are not. The reasons for this are multiple, and include the following:

- Extreme weather related crash costs appear in crash statistics and are hence accounted for in purely statistical sense. However, the marginal impact of extreme weather to crash incidence is not clear and measures that purely improve traffic safety might not have any material impact on weather-related crashes. In Kreuz et al. (2012) it was estimated that 10%-20% of all road crashes are more or less attributed to adverse weather conditions.

- Extreme weather-induced time delays of freight affect shippers' costs, amounting to significant cumulative annual figures (Nokkala et al., 2012). These costs are borne by actors outside the transport system and therefore they can be regarded as externalised.
- Increased maintenance costs are in many cases borne by private sector contractors, especially when road or other infrastructure managers have outsourced day-to-day maintenance services to private service providers. This has been done widely in some countries e.g. in Sweden and Finland, both at national level and municipality level. To win the fixed-period maintenance contracts, the contractors cannot or will not include extreme weather risk premiums in their contract prices and in the worst cases cover the negative cash flows themselves. These costs do not appear in any calculations. It is an outsourced risk from the perspective of infrastructure managers but a socio-economic loss as a whole.

Difference in policy and managerial decision tools

In most cases, extreme weather or climate change risks are not a part of the project appraisal methods and this reflects the difference in policy statements and tools put to work in practice. An example of this was pointed out in Leviäkangas and Hautala (2011) concerning environmental externalities in transport sector in Finland. The pricing regime (taxes on vehicles and fuels) and policy commitments forcefully favour greener transport, but when investments are made for example in road infrastructure, the standard appraisal method clearly prioritises efficiency-enhancing (i.e. time-saving) projects. Environmental benefits account approximately only 1% of the identified benefits of Finland's greenfield road projects. The analysis stated:

> Even if climate change could be challenged in many respects, there is a possibility, a risk, that the change is real. This should be reflected in price, as do the risks of future prospects in the prices of shares quoted in stock market. Hence, the unit cost values (prices) of emitted tons and persons exposed should be lifted to a level that corresponds to the policy targets when making public investments (Leviäkangas and Hautala, 2011).

This analysis underlines that policy objectives may be misaligned with the outcome of CBA especially when the latter assumes prices and weights that are not reflective of societal preferences and appetite for risk.

Extreme weather risks and time value of money

Standard CBA calculations are based on discounting future flows of cash or non-cash based costs and benefits, using two principal risk appraisal techniques: either by risk-adjusting the required return on investment (the discounting rate) or, or by including probabilistic risks (e.g. the expected costs) into the equation. Both methods work in principle, but are applicable to different contexts.

Risk-adjusting of discounting rates is a demanding exercise. Any risk can be argued to be valid for adjusting the rate, but not all risks should be incorporated into CBA. Adjusting can be done for uncertainty regarding to-be-realised costs or benefits (volatility), demand risk, technological risk, etc. The common denominator for all these risks is *time*, as "the nature of things" defines that all these risks are increasing as a function of time.

"Time risk" means that the longer the time period considered, the more uncertain are the states-of-the-world that lay the basis for future projections. In other words, the further to the future we aim, the greater the uncertainty of hitting the target. In strictly financial investments this logic is self-evident: it is riskier to invest one's money for 30 years than for three years. For transport investments, this issue has been analysed in the context of investments in intelligent transport systems (ITS). ITS investments have typically much shorter life span than conventional infrastructure investments and therefore there are grounds to risk-adjust the discounting rate downwards for ITS investments (see e.g. Leviäkangas and Lähesmaa, 2002), thus making ITS investments time-wise less risky than traditional infrastructure investments. For extreme weather and particularly climate change related analysis time risk is of relevance as the phenomena are not only uncertain but also perhaps far away in the future.

"Volatility risk" may be associated directly with time risk (for the far-away future) but it also may be associated with expected volatility of costs and/or benefits, which of course are uncertain just like most assumptions regarding the future. But the costs of extreme weather bear precisely this risk volatility: the costs can be more or less as expected or they can be completely out of the normal range of expectations, massive in scope and exceeding all expectations. Potential savings in these costs deserves attention in cost-benefit analysis. There are scientists that have analysed extreme events and some of the results suggest that our perception of weather extremes in fact underestimates their frequency (Makkonen, 2006; 2008), but there is no consensus among researchers regarding this finding.

The most pragmatic stakeholder group, which is also familiar with economic risk assessment, is the project finance community. Financiers, for the most part, approach risk operationalisation through adjusting their required returns according to risk-return theory, first introduced by Markowitz (1959). Public investors, such as transport agencies, face difficulty in changing the standard cost-benefit analysis procedures and are not familiar with risk-adjusting their discounting rates, though in principle this should be possible (Stiglitz, 1994). But in practice, public investors' required returns – the social discounting rates – are kept constant and applied as such thus disregarding the varying risk profiles of projects. In this context, public investors' alternative is to include the expected costs of extreme weather events as cost items in their cost-benefit calculations.

The selection of discounting rate is a managerial decision, and for social discounting rates to be used for public investments the situation is identical. Each country and their public body investors must decide on how much they require return for public investments. In Finland, for example, the discount rate has been set at 4% for all transport sector state investments across the modes (Finnish Transport Agency, 2011). The rate was lowered from 5% and residual values are estimated based on true expected technical life of the sub-asset after 30 years. Infrastructure projects are divided to sub-components, e.g. sub-structures, bridges, culverts, pavements. For instance, if the expected life of a bridge in a road project is 80 years and the cost estimate is EUR 20 million, the present residual value with 4% discounting rate of the bridge in cost-benefit calculus is EUR 20 million × (80-30) a / 80 a × 0.308 = EUR 3.85 million. This calculus is repeated across the sub-components of the project.

The changes made to the previous guidelines make long-term evaluation more feasible than previously. Also the unit values for crashes, time and environmental factors have been raised by 1.5% annually for the 30 year standard s period. The choice of discount rates and how to handle residual values are key parameters in the long-term appraisal of infrastructure projects using CBA. Keeping the rates low and including the residual values in the project appraisal gives an entirely different perspective with regard to life cycle management of the infrastructure.

ITF (2014) formulates two specific strategies for improving CBA in light of uncertainty surrounding climate change and extreme weather events. The first involves undertaking uncertainty assessments that evaluate both the range of scientific uncertainty on hazards and socio-economic uncertainty regarding impacts and exposure. Due to the nature of the uncertainties considered, these assessments cannot simply be slotted into existing CBA as quantitative inputs, but can qualify the results of CBA with guidance on confidence regarding the results of the exercise. In terms of addressing the selection of discount rates, the report points to two potential pathways for improving CBA in light of uncertainty: applying a risk premium to selected discount rates or applying a subjective probability distribution over the objective probability distribution for the discount rate in order to capture inherent uncertainty ranges. Neither of these approaches fully addresses challenges posed by deep uncertainty but they do help adapt traditional CBA to project appraisal in light of climate and extreme weather impacts.

Generally CBA is most useful for assessing adaptation options when climate probabilities are known, climate sensitivity is assumed to be small compared to costs and benefits, good quality data exists for the major cost-benefit categories and agreement is high on valuation scales for costs, benefits and discount rates (Watkiss et al., 2012)

Cost-effectiveness analysis

When achieving agreement on monetary evaluation is difficult or impossible, cost-effectiveness analysis (CEA) can provide a way to weigh the relative value of various options. CEA compares and ranks alternative for achieving similar outcomes. Typically, CEA allows options to be ranked along a single comparable metric – e.g. cost per unit of desired outcome. These marginal abatement curves are particularly helpful in charting the least-cost path to achieving a set of desired outcomes. CEA can also identify the highest impact options from a range of considered measures and thus can guide resources to where they deliver the biggest benefits at the lowest cost.

However, while suited for prioritising GHG mitigation options, among others, CEA is perhaps less well suited for assessing adaptation measures. This is partly due to the fact that its reductive focus on a single metric makes it difficult to account for regional and local specificities and leaves out a number of costs and benefits that cannot adequately be captured in a benefit per cost of unit approach. For instance, cost effectiveness metrics to measure reduction of flood risk or impacts from sea level rise or storm surge could include exposure metrics (cost to reduce the potentially flooded area, cost to reduce the percentage of the population exposed to flooding) or economic metrics (cost to reduce expected annual damages). Alternatively, the metric could focus on reducing impacts (cost per land area unit relative to the value of the protected land). Another possibility could include the cost to limit flooding to a pre-determined threshold. All of these metrics present challenges in assessing impacts, precisely due to the uncertainty of climate risk and some also include the added challenge of determining acceptable levels of risk and/or protection. Indeed, by relying on single cost curves based on central estimates for a single or a selection of emission scenarios, CEA fails to account for the fundamentally uncertain nature of many climate change impacts. Further, when looking across the broad range of potential climate change impacts, it becomes difficult to select and prioritise CEA metrics across impact vectors. While CEA has been used in some non-transport adaptation contexts (e.g. health impact metrics or acceptable levels of flood risk metrics) it is not clear that it is any better – or worse – suited for adaptation appraisal than CBA which enjoys wider use (Watkiss et al., 2012).

In addition to the contexts in which CBA is useful, CEA can be helpful for assessing adaptation when a high level of agreement exists on social objectives (e.g. broad acceptance of risk thresholds), when a reduced set of impact is being considered and when the timeframes or impacts being considered are less subject to deep uncertainty.

Multi-criteria analysis

Multi-criteria analysis (MCA) is particularly well suited for assessing options using both quantitative and qualitative information. MCA provides a systematic methodology for assessing and ranking options against a range of scoring criteria that may be expressed in monetary units or in qualitative weights. In many cases, MCA is used in conjunction with traditional CBA to capture impacts that are difficult to monetise. Because it allows the consideration of a much broader range of criteria than CBA or CEA, MCA can be useful for assessing options in the absence of a market or shadow prices. It also by its nature encourages consultation across a wide range of stakeholders. However, the scoring and weighting exercise always remains somewhat subjective even if an effort is made to make the process as transparent as possible. It can also be cumbersome to carry out due to the consultation process. In particular MCA may not be well suited for capturing uncertainty in any other than a subjective manner.

Tools and approaches for decision making under uncertainty

All three traditional decision-support tools discussed in the prior section, while familiar to many transport decision-makers and planners, are generally not well-suited to handling the deep uncertainty that characterises many climate change adaptation decisions. For this reason, there is growing interest in alternative appraisal frameworks that better capture this aspect of adaptation planning.

Table 4.1. **Traditional vs. adaptive attitudes for transport appraisal**

Decision making in predictable contexts	Decision making under uncertainty
Seek precise predictions	Uncover a range of possibilities
Build prediction from detailed understanding	Predict from experience with aggregate responses
Promote scientific consensus	Embrace alternatives
Minimise conflict among actors	Highlight difficult trade-offs
Emphasise short-term objectives	Promote long-term objectives
Presume certainty in seeking the best outcome	Account-for and evaluate future feedback and learning
Define best outcomes from a predictable set of alternatives	Seek outliers
	Expect and design for change
Seek productive equilibrium	

Source: Walters, 1986.

Walters (1986) describes the main features of the types of decision making frameworks that work well under predictable circumstances compared to those that are better able to handle deep uncertainty on impacts and inputs.

Table 4.2. **Summary of tools adapted to decision making under uncertainty**

Real-options analysis	Allows economic analysis of future option value and economic benefit of waiting, gathering more information and flexibility
Robust decision making	Identifies robust (rather than optimal) decisions under deep uncertainty, by stress testing a large number of scenarios
Portfolio analysis	Assessment of an optimal blend of portfolios of options by trade-off between return (net present value) and uncertainty (variance)
Iterative risk (adaptive) management	Uses monitoring, research, evaluation and learning to better adapt future strategies to scenarios and risk thresholds

Source: Watkiss et al., 2012.

In their comprehensive review, Watkiss et al. (2012) builds on earlier work by Hallegatte (2009) and others to map out "new" appraisal approaches that display better aptitude to handle climate uncertainty. They identify several potential approaches, four of which are outlined in Table 4.2 and summarised in Table 4.3. Two of these approaches, real options analysis and robust decision making, seem well suited for transport-related adaptation appraisal.

Real-options analysis

Real-options analysis (ROA) is rooted in options-based approaches from financial markets. In the latter, an option gives investors the right, but not the obligation, to acquire an asset in the future. This serves to help buffer against market volatility and uncertainty regarding the value of assets over time. The flexibility in exercising the option is the source of the option's market value. Similarly, investments in physical assets may benefit from flexibility in light of future uncertainty. Because with time, society will gain better knowledge about the scale and scope of climate impacts, real-options analysis ("real" because it deals with physical as opposed to financial assets) incorporates this flexibility into decision making and may usefully serve to guide certain climate change adaptation efforts.

This flexibility refers both to the timing of the investment decision ("build now" vs. "build later") as well as to the ability for the infrastructure to adjust to changing conditions over time (e.g. "build for, but not with"). Accounting for this flexibility may yield different investment decisions than under traditional and deterministic economic appraisal techniques. ROA analysis may indicate that it makes sense to put off an investment until such time when better information about climate change impacts becomes available. It may also indicate that it is worth proceeding with the initial stages of a project (or phasing a project so that it may be deployed over several discrete stages) despite a weak traditional economic appraisal score in order to keep the option of further developing or completing the project alive. For instance, ROA analysis may support building a seawall such that it can be retrofitted at a later date to better account for rising sea level and increased incidences of storm surges. An upgradeable seawall will cost more upfront than a traditional seawall and this may cause this option to fail a standard CBA test. In the context of uncertainty, however, it may cost less to invest more upfront in this option (see Box 4.1).

The value of putting off an investment will be greater if the time to acquisition of new information is shorter and the higher the degree of uncertainty over outcomes. There is a cost to putting off an investment stemming from the delayed delivery of the services or other benefits the investment would have delivered. There is also an opportunity cost from over-investing in an initial phase of a project that must be weighed against the benefit of reduced investment at a future date should one uncertain option play itself out. These trade-offs can be captured with various computational decision-tree methods. Projects should proceed if ROA analysis indicates that the overall lost value from benefits during the waiting time is superior to the value of waiting or, alternatively, that that the option value derived from a series of optimal choices at multiple decision-points marking each phase in a multi-phase project is greater than the standard appraised value of average returns over the life of the project (Watkiss et al., 2012).

Real-options analysis is particularly suited for large, up-front and irreversible investments; it has been used in assessing investments in dikes and large-scale hydraulic projects. However, because probabilities must be assigned to specific outcomes, the formal application of ROA requires probabilistic inputs regarding climate impacts and therefore may be less suited to cases where deep uncertainty exists.

Box 4.1. **Appraisal using a real-options analysis**

Consider a proposal for investing in infrastructure protecting against the impacts of flooding due to climate change. There are two options: invest in a wall, or invest in a wall which has the option to upgrade in the future. There is an equal probability of high or low climate change impacts in the future. The standard wall costs 75, and has benefits of 100 from avoided flooding. The upgradeable wall costs 50, the upgrade costs 50 and would give benefits of 200 from avoided flooding. The discount rate is 0.8.

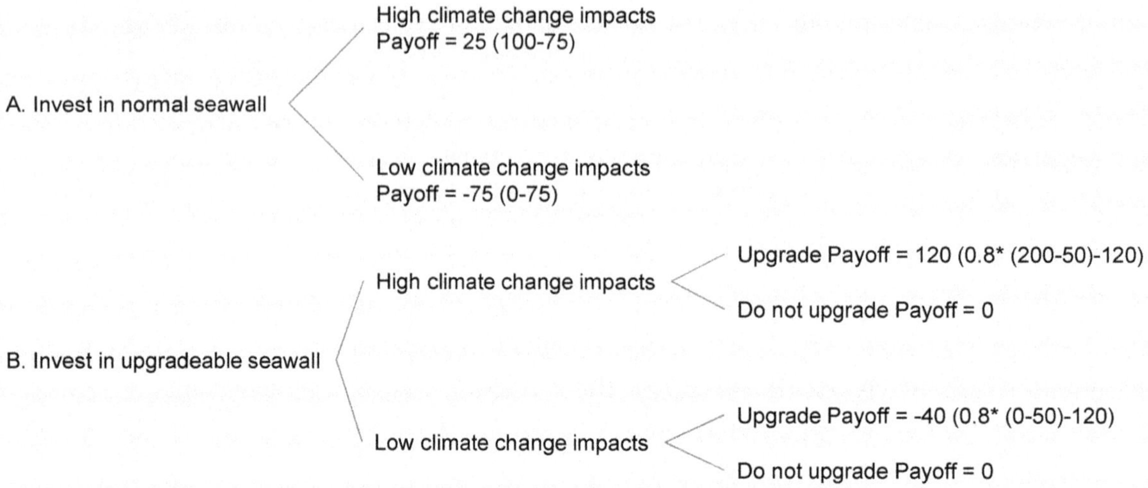

The expected value of investing in the standard wall is a simple net present value (NPV) calculation, calculating the expected costs and benefits of the investment. The NPV is (0.5*25) + (0.5*-75) = -25. This suggests the investment should not proceed. Flexibility over the investment decision allows the possibility to upgrade in the future if the impacts of climate change are high. The expected value of this option can be calculated.

If the impacts of climate change are high enough to warrant upgrading, then the value of the investment is 120. If the impacts are low, then upgrading is not justified since the payoff is negative (-40). Since the investment costs of the upgrade are not realised in practice in the low outcome, they are therefore not incorporated into the NPV. The expected value of investing now with the option to upgrade in the future is (0.5*120) – 50 = +10.

Comparing the two approaches shows an NPV of -25 for the standard approach, and +10 for the real-options approach. Flexibility to upgrade in the future is reflected in the higher NPV and switches the investment decision.

Source: HM Treasury, 2009.

Robust decision making

Robust decision making (RDM) is an alternative approach that is adapted to situations where no probabilistic information exists regarding impacts or outcomes. RDM seeks to select those strategies and investments that are consistently robust under the widest range of plausible climate outcomes and impacts. RDM represents an alternative "agree on outcomes" approach to decision making where outcomes are selected first and then tested for robustness. In this way, it avoids having to find consensus on future climate change impacts which otherwise hampers "agree on assumption"-based approaches. Because RDM obviates the need to select probabilities of outcomes, it is especially well-suited to decisions characterised by deep uncertainty. Crucially, RDM may favour outcomes that are optimal in no single situation but that are good enough in most circumstances. RDM seeks to minimise regrets rather than optimise specific (but perhaps vulnerable) outcomes.

RDM is computationally heavy as multiple scenarios entailing complex decision outcomes must be modelled. This may be less of a constraint as even large-scale and complex calculations have been accelerated by parallelised processing and use of cloud-based servers. Nonetheless, RDM requires a high level of expert knowledge on potential outcomes of investment decisions under multiple contexts and their inter-relationships.

Methodologically, RDM iterates analysis of decision outcomes over multiple potential future scenarios based on a multi-step approach (see Figure 4.2).

Figure 4.2. **The process of robust decision making**

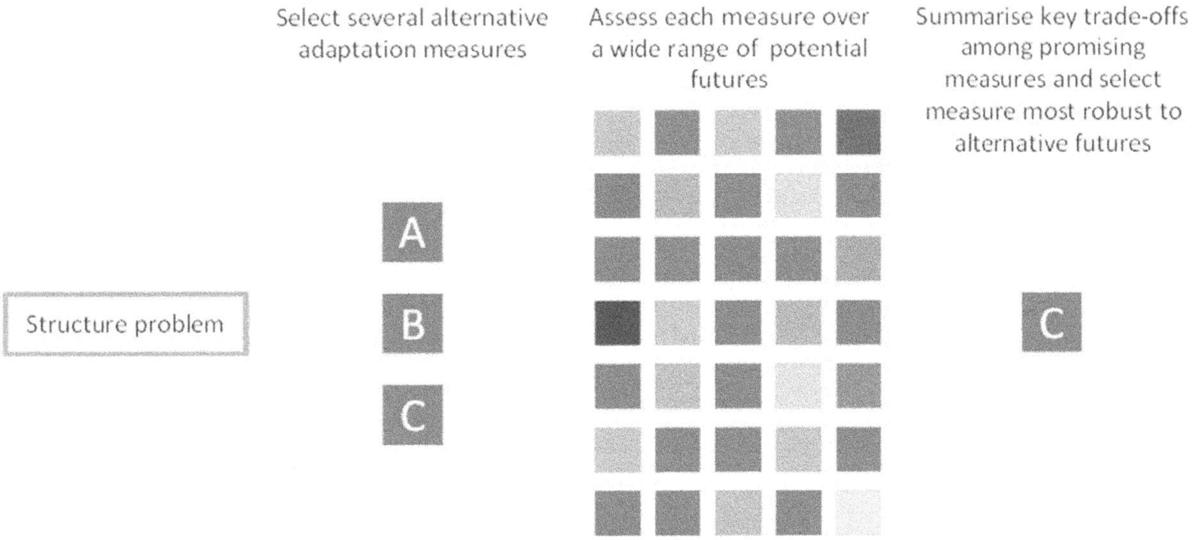

Source: Adapted from Groves et al., 2008.

RDM starts out by characterising the problem to be addressed (e.g. a climate change impact to be mitigated) and, rather than seek to establish a probabilistic range of future scenarios to which the decision on a strategy or measure must be adapted, it looks at describing a variety of potential measures. Each measure is then assessed over a wide range of computer-generated future scenarios. This "stress test" helps to determine which combination of uncertainty parameters are most important to the choices between strategies. Based on this exercise, one or several, measures can be selected that are best able to deliver desired outcomes across the widest range of possible futures. Selected outcomes may be optimal under no specific scenario but "good enough" under the widest range of futures. Because it enables insight to be gained from situations characterised by deep uncertainty, RDM is best suited for those situations where specific climate impacts are highly uncertain – like precipitation.

Though some cases exist, neither ROA nor RDM have worked their way into widespread project appraisal for transport infrastructure at this time. There are many reasons for this, including the regulatory structure governing appraisal and insurance requirements regarding risk assessment. Work therefore remains to understand how best these approaches can be integrated into transport investment appraisal.

Table 4.3. **Summary overview of decision support tools for the appraisal of climate change and extreme weather adaptation strategies**

Tool	Strengths	Weaknesses	Most useful when
Cost-benefit analysis	Provides direct analysis of economic, benefits, justification for action, and optimal solutions. Well known and widely applied.	Difficulty of monetary valuation for non-market sectors and non-technical options. Uncertainty usually limited to probabilistic risks.	Climate probabilities known. Climate sensitivity small compared to costs/benefits. Good data exists for major cost/benefit components.
Cost-effectiveness analysis	Benefits expressed in physical terms (not monetary) thus applicable to non-market sectors. Relatively simple to apply and easily understandable ranking and outputs. Use of cost curves can assess policy targets with least-cost optimisation. Used for mitigation, thus widely recognised and resonance with policy makers.	Benefits can be difficult to identify and single metric does not capture all costs and benefits. Less applicable cross-sectoral/complex risks. Works best with technical options, and often omits capacity building and soft measures. Sequential nature of cost curves ignores interlinkages and potential for portfolios. Does not lend itself to the consideration of uncertainty, as works with central tendency.	Same as CBA, but for nonmonetary metrics. Agreement on sectoral social objective (e.g. acceptable risks of flooding).
Multi-criteria analysis	Combines quantitative and qualitative data,; monetary and non-monetary units, thus applicable where quantification is challenging. Relatively simple and transparent, and relatively low cost/time requirement. Expert judgement can be used very efficiently, and involves stakeholders, thus can be based on local knowledge.	Results need further interpretation and elaboration in more detailed studies. Different experts may have different opinions, i.e. subjectivity involved. Stakeholders may lack knowledge and can miss important options. Analysis of uncertainty is often qualitative and subjective.	Mix of qualitative and quantification data.

Table 4.3. **Summary overview of decision support tools for the appraisal of climate change and extreme weather adaptation strategies (continued)**

Tool	Strengths	Weaknesses	Most useful when
Real-options analysis	Assesses value of flexibility and learning, in quantitative and economic terms. Decision trees conceptualise and visualise the concept of adaptive management.	Data and resource intensive, with high complexity and expert input. Data a potential barrier, (probabilistic climate, quantitative and economic information). Identification decision points often complex.	Large irreversible capital decisions. Climate risk probabilities known or good information. - Good quality data for major cost/benefit components.
Robust decision making	Assesses robustness rather than optimisation. Applicable where probabilistic information is low or missing, or climate uncertainty is high. Can work with physical or economic metrics, enhancing application across sectors.	Lack of quantitative probabilities can make more subjective, influenced by stakeholders. The formal application has a high demand for quantitative information, computing power, and requires a high degree of expert knowledge.	High uncertainty of climate change signal. Mix of quantitative and qualitative information. Non-market sectors (e.g. ecosystems, health).
Portfolio analysis	Assesses portfolios, which analysis of individual adaptation options not allow. Measures "returns" using various metrics, including physical or economic, thus broad applicability. Use of the efficiency frontier an effective way of visualising results and risk-return trade-offs.	Resource intensive and needs expert knowledge. Relies on the availability of quantitative data (effectiveness and variance/co-variance). Requires probabilistic climate information, or an assumption of likelihood equivalence. Issues of inter-dependence between options.	Adaptation actions likely to be complementary in reducing climate risks. Climate risk probabilities known or good information.

Table 4.3. **Summary overview of decision support tools for the appraisal of climate change and extreme weather adaptation strategies (continued)**

Tool	Strengths	Weaknesses	Most useful when
Adaptive management	Process of monitoring, research, evaluation and learning that avoids irreversible decisions and encourages learning to adjust decisions over time. Uses scenarios to delineate uncertainties not to predict the future. Is more policy orientated and flexible in objectives and appraisal methods Encourages discussion about (un)acceptable change and definition of critical indicators.	Challenging when multiple risks acting together, or indirect links to climate change. Thresholds are not always easy to identify, especially those that are poorly defined. Focuses on existing management objectives. Unknown impacts and new challenges may be overlooked/difficult. Loses simplicity for communication less well defined thresholds and multiple drivers./	High uncertainty. Clear risk thresholds and indicators. Mix of quantitative and qualitative information.

Source: Watkiss et al., 2012.

References

Finnish Transport Agency (2011), "Liikenneväylien hankearvioinnin yleisohje" [Guidelines for transport project evaluation]. Guidelines of the Finnish Transport Agency 14-2011.

Frankhauser, S., J.B. Smith and R.S.J. Tol (1999), "Weathering Climate Change: Some simple rules to guide adaptation decisions". *Ecological Economics*, Vol. 30, pp. 67-78.

Groves, D., G. Lempert, R. Knopman and S. Berry (2008), "Preparing for an Uncertain Future Climate in the Inland Empire: Identifying Robust Water Management Strategies". Rand Corporation, Santa Monica.

Hallegatte, S. (2009), "Strategies to Adapt to an Uncertain Climate". *Global Environmental Change*, Vol. 19.

HM Treasury (2009), "Accounting for the Effects of Climate Change: Supplementary Green Book Guidance", HM Treasury, Department for Environment Food and Rural Affairs, Pubs, London.

ITF (2015), *Adapting Transport Policy to Climate Change: Carbon Valuation, Risk and Uncertainty*, OECD Publishing, Paris.
DOI: http://dx.doi.org/10.1787/9789282107928-en

Kreuz, M. et al. (2012), EWENT D3 - Consequences of extreme weather. DLR Forschungsbericht 2012-03. German Aerospace Center.

Leviäkangas, P. and R. Hautala (2011), "Eco-Pricing of Mobility". *International Journal of Technology*. Vol. 2/2, Universitas Indonesia.

Leviäkangas, P. and J. Lähesmaa (2002), "Profitability Evaluation of Intelligent Transport System Investments". *ASCE Journal of Transportation Engineering*. Vol. 128/3.

Makkonen, L. (2006), "Plotting Positions in Extreme Value Analysis", *Journal of Applied Meteorology and Climatology*. Vol. 45/2, pp. 334-340.

Makkonen, L. (2008), "Problems in the Extreme Value Analysis", *Structural Safety*, Vol. 30, pp. 405-419.

Markowitz, H. (1959), *Portfolio Selection: Efficient Diversification of Investments*. Yale University Press, New Haven.

Nokkala, M., P. Leviäkangas and K. Oiva (eds.) (2012), "The costs of extreme weather for the European transport system". – EWENT project D4, VTT Technology 36. VTT.

Patt, A., J. Hinkel and R. Swart (2011), "Mediation Deleverable 4.1: Report on Uncertainty Methods".

Stiglitz, J.E. (1994), "Discount Rates: The Rate of Discount for Benefit-Cost Analysis and the Theory of Second Best", in *Cost-Benefit Analysis*, (2nd ed.), Layard, R. and S. Glaister (eds.), Cambridge University Press, Cambridge, pp. 116-159.

Walker, W. et al. (2003), "Defining Uncertainty: A Conceptual Basis for Uncertainty Management in Model-Based Decision Support". *Integrated Assessment*, Vol. 4/1.

Walters, C.J. (1986), *Adaptive Management of Renewable Resources*. Blackburn Press.

Watkiss, P. et al. (2012), *Framework for Costs, Cost Effectiveness and Other Methods (Including Taking Into Account Uncertainties) for Socio-economic Assessmenty*. Stockholm Environment Institute, Oxford.

Glossary

Anthropogenic: Caused, resulting from or related to the influence of humans on nature.

Climate: The statistical expression in terms of means and variability of observations of temperature, precipitation, cloudiness and wind over a given period – 30 years as set in standard practice is the period used to define climate "normal" by the World Meteorological Organization. It is in essence "long-term average weather conditions" that can be characteristically be found in specific geographic zones or altitude bands.

Climate change: When measurements of climate variability reveal persistent "anomalous" conditions in reference to regional climate parameters (conditions that do not fit in the historic record of climate variability), the climate is said to be changing. The revelation of "climate change" is therefore dependent upon a reference state – or more precisely a reference period. In terms of measuring the anthropogenic influence of GHG emissions on climate change, the reference period has typically been the latter part of the pre-industrial period (~ climate of the late 18th early-19th century). For detecting ongoing changes in climate, the reference state is typically the most recent 30-year "climate normal" period as defined by the World Meteorological Organization. All measurements of climate change are sensitive to starting and end dates due to natural variability and for this reason, longer time periods are preferred for climate change assessment. Simply put, weather observations, when averaged over a 30 or more year period are the basis for defining "climate" and this statistical definition, in turn, is used to express extreme weather occurrences and provides the baseline against which long-term changes in climate are measured.

Climate variability: The World Meteorological Organization defines climate variability as "variations in the mean state and other statistics (such as standard deviations and the occurrence of extremes) of the climate on all temporal and spatial scales beyond that of individual weather events. The term is often used to denote deviations of climatic statistics over a given period of time (e.g. a month, season or year) from the long-term statistics relating to the corresponding calendar period. In this sense, climate variability is measured by those deviations, which are usually termed anomalies. Variability may be due to natural internal processes within the climate system (internal variability), or to variations in natural or anthropogenic external forcing (external variability)".

Cryosphere: The cryosphere is comprised of all of the frozen surfaces of the earth, including areas covered by ice sheets and glaciers, permafrost regions, and sea areas covered by ice, at least in winter.

El Niño/La Niña: The US National Oceanic and Atmospheric Administration defines El Niño and La Niña as opposite phases of what is known as the El Niño-Southern Oscillation (ENSO) cycle. The ENSO cycle is a scientific term that describes the fluctuations in temperature between the ocean and atmosphere in the east-central Equatorial Pacific. La Niña is sometimes referred to as the cold phase of ENSO and El Niño as the warm phase of ENSO. These deviations from normal surface temperatures can have large-scale impacts not only on ocean processes, but also on global weather and climate.

Exposure: In terms of this report, exposure is the presence of physical infrastructure assets or transport-related activities in places that could be adversely affected by climate-related hazards (IPCC, 2014; 2012). In terms of risk management, exposure is a necessary variable in order to determine risk. If there is no exposure to a hazard, then the hazard continues to exist but poses no risk (Ropeik and Gray, 2002).

Extreme weather (event): A weather event that through its intensity or scale places it at the outlying part of the distribution of similar observed events for a set temporal range and locale. For instance, one way of defining extreme weather events are those that are as rare as or rarer than the 10th and 90th percentiles of the observed probability distribution for a reference period.

Hazard: An event or process that may create damage or losses (Ropeik and Gray, 2002). In the context of this report, weather and hazards are not synonymous though extreme weather incidents may lead to the occurrence of hazards: e.g. rain and temperature are weather variables that in their extreme may lead to hazards such as flooding or heat waves. Likewise, sea level rise is a climate-related phenomenon but coastal flooding is a hazard linked to sea level rise.

Radiative forcing: The Intergovernmental Panel on Climate Change defines radiative forcing as "the change in net (down minus up) irradiance (solar plus longwave; in W m–2) at the tropopause after allowing for stratospheric temperatures to readjust to radiative equilibrium, but with surface and tropospheric temperatures and state held fixed at the unperturbed values".

Resilience: In the context of this report, resilience connotes the ability for infrastructure or transport networks to adjust easily to or recover rapidly from negative impacts linked to climate or weather-related hazards.

Risk: The function of a hazard and exposure to that hazard. In terms of this report, it refers to the probability of deleterious impacts of hazards on transport infrastructure and networks (Ropeik and Gray, 2002). Probabilistic risk refers to risks that can be quantified and statistically described via a probability distribution.

Robustness: Infrastructure or networks that are robust are sturdily constructed in such a way as to perform without failure under a wide range of conditions.

Uncertainty or "deep" uncertainty: Describes outcomes whose probability of occurring cannot be quantified or characterised by a probability distribution. These are outcomes for which insufficient information exists as to the likelihood of their realisation or not.

Vulnerability: The propensity or predisposition to be adversely affected by a hazard (IPCC, 2014). It is a function of the character and magnitude of a hazard, exposure to that hazard and its capacity to adapt or otherwise absorb the damaging impacts of that hazard.

Weather: The state of the atmosphere at a given time and place with regards to temperature, precipitation, cloudiness and wind.

Working Group Members

Mr. J.B. WLASCHIN Chair
Director, Office of Asset Management
Federal Highway Administration
U.S. Department of Transportation
HIAM-1 Room E75-340
1200 New Jersey Avenue, S.E.
20590 WASHINGTON D.C.
United States

Pr. Michael A.P. TAYLOR
Em. Pr. Michael A.P. TAYLOR
School of Natural and Built Environments
City East campus
University of South Australia
GPO Box 2471
SA 5001 ADELAIDE
Australia

Mr. Bill DWYER
Project Manager,
Surface Infrastructure Programs
Transport Canada
330, SPARKS STREET TOWER C
K1A ON5 OTTAWA
Canada

Dr. Pekka LEVIÄKANGAS

Chief Research Scientist, Team Leader

VTT Technical Research Centre of Finland

Kaitoväylä 1

90571 OULU

Finland

Dr. Ariane DUPONT-KIEFFER

Research

Transport Economics of Sociology Department (DEST)

French Institute of Science and Technology for Transport, Development and Networks (IFSTTAR)

Le Descartes II

2 rue de la Butte Verte

93166 NOISY-LE-GRAND cedex

France

Ms. Gabriele GRIMM

Deputy Research Commissioner

Research Policy, Programme Management

Federal Ministry of Transport, Building and Urban Development

Robert-Schuman-Platz 1

D-53175 BONN

Germany

Dr. Sebastian KOFALK

U2 - Ecological Interactions

Federal Institute of Hydrology

Bundesanstalt für Gewässerkunde

Am Mainzer Tor 1

56068 KOBLENZ

Germany

Mr. Shinri SONE
Director, Road Environment Division
National Institute for Land and Infrastructure Management (NILIM)
Ministry Land Infrastructure and Transport (MLIT)
1 Asahi, Tsukuba-shi
305-0804 IBARAKI PREF.
Japan

Mr. Sungwon LEE
Senior Reseach Fellow
Korean Transport Institute (KOTI)
23-11 Daewha - Dong
GOYANG – CITY
Korea

Mr. Albert COMPTE
Director
Centre of Studies on Applied Techniques
Center for Research and Experimentation of Public Works (CEDEX)
Alfonso XII, 3-5
28014 MADRID
Spain

ITF Research and Policy

Mr. Stephen PERKINS
Head Research and Policy
2 rue André-Pascal
75016 Paris

Mr. Philippe CRIST
Economist

Mr. Jari KAUPPILA
Economist

Melle Sylène LASFARGUES

Intern

Mme Dominique BOUQUET

Assistant

Other contributors:

Denis FRANÇOIS

Institut Français des Sciences et Technologies des Transports, de l'Aménagement et des Réseaux

IFSTTAR

France

Matthew KARLAFTIS

Department of Transportation

Engineering, National Technical

University of Athens

Greece

Gordana PETKOVIC

Staff Director

Norwegian Public Roads Administration

Norway

Michelle WITTON-SMITH

Department for Transport (DfT)

United Kingdom

Ms. Eva RUIZ-AYÚCAR

Spain

Mr.Harald KOETHE
Bundesministerium für Verkehr, Bau und Stadtenwicklung
Germany

Mr.Robert KAFALENOS
Environmental Protection Specialist
U.S. Department of Transportation
United States

Mr.Michael JOHNSEN
Department of Transportation
United States

Mr.James CLARKIN
Transport Canada
Canada

Ms. Cheryl ALLEN RICHTER
Federal Highway Administration, Turner-Fairbank Highway Research Center
United States

ORGANISATION FOR ECONOMIC CO-OPERATION AND DEVELOPMENT

The OECD is a unique forum where governments work together to address the economic, social and environmental challenges of globalisation. The OECD is also at the forefront of efforts to understand and to help governments respond to new developments and concerns, such as corporate governance, the information economy and the challenges of an ageing population. The Organisation provides a setting where governments can compare policy experiences, seek answers to common problems, identify good practice and work to co-ordinate domestic and international policies.

The OECD member countries are: Australia, Austria, Belgium, Canada, Chile, the Czech Republic, Denmark, Estonia, Finland, France, Germany, Greece, Hungary, Iceland, Ireland, Israel, Italy, Japan, Korea, Latvia, Luxembourg, Mexico, the Netherlands, New Zealand, Norway, Poland, Portugal, the Slovak Republic, Slovenia, Spain, Sweden, Switzerland, Turkey, the United Kingdom and the United States. The European Union takes part in the work of the OECD.

OECD Publishing disseminates widely the results of the Organisation's statistics gathering and research on economic, social and environmental issues, as well as the conventions, guidelines and standards agreed by its members.

OECD PUBLISHING, 2, rue André-Pascal, 75775 PARIS CEDEX 16
(74 2016 01 1 P) ISBN 978-92-82-10806-2 – 2016

www.ingramcontent.com/pod-product-compliance
Ingram Content Group UK Ltd.
Pitfield, Milton Keynes, MK11 3LW, UK
UKHW051505290926
15471UKWH00008B/1420

9 789282 108062